Hypnosis and Hypnotherapy

The Power of the Subconscious mind

Philip Holder, Ph.D.

Published by
The Institute of Hypnosis Sciences

Copyright 2002

Master's Realm Books

PO Box 992

Morrisville, PA 19067

Copyright Philip Holder

All rights reserved. No part of this book may be reproduced, or transmitted in any form, including but not limited to, electronic, print, or mechanical means, without the express written permission of Dr. Philip Holder.

Printed in the United States of America

Registered with Library of Congress

Disclaimer

This book is for educational purposes only. It is not intended to take the place of a qualified personal instructor. The author, publishers, marketers etc. accept no responsibility or liability for any actions of the reader should he or she attempt to utilize information contained in this book. Laws and requirements for various modalities differ by jurisdiction therefore it is advisable for those utilizing hypnotherapy to investigate the legal requirements in your area before practicing. A previous knowledge of the basics of hypnosis are helpful in understanding the content of this book.

DEDICATION

I would like to dedicate this book to my three extraordinary children, Brandon, Samantha, and Ashley.
Being a father to such wonderful children is a blessing beyond anything that words can express.

Love Ya,
Dad

Table of Contents

Forward

There are many books and videos on the topics of hypnosis and hypnotherapy. Many of them approach hypnosis as if it were a mystical power. I prefer to approach it as a science. There are certain principals and concepts that are fundamental to hypnosis and to its use as a therapeutic medium. Understanding how hypnosis works is essential in one's ability to utilize its tremendous potential to help others.

Inducing hypnosis is only the beginning. For clients or patients to benefit from hypnosis therapeutically, it is important that the hypnotist or therapist have an understanding of how the subconscious mind differs from the conscious mind. What we perceive as reality is our reality. When we change perception, we can easily (and almost automatically) change behavior and response. Perception is a component of the subconscious mind. For permanent behavioral change to take place it is only common sense to recognize that the most effective and efficient way to make positive change is at the subconscious level. That is where hypnosis comes in.

When students attend my classes, lectures, and workshops they frequently approach me and say that they enjoyed my class because the information that I taught them was material they could actually take back and use in their practice on a day-to-day basis. My purpose in writing this book and in creating the companion video to this book was to provide the same practical material that I strive to offer when I teach a class. I don't remember who said it, but I remember reading that the man who can read fine literature and doesn't, is no better off than the man who cannot read. Similarly, knowledge is only of real value when it can be applied.

More than being a "How To" book, it is my hope that you the reader will, after reading this book, have a better understanding of the hypnotic process. Although "how to" information is provided, greater benefit will be accomplished by expanding your base of knowledge and your understanding of this fascinating subject. Through understanding the process rather than imitating what others have done, one can accomplish truly amazing things and potentially rise to levels never before experienced.

Sincerely,
Philip Holder, Ph.D.

Chapter 1

Introduction to Hypnosis and Hypnotherapy
The Conscious and the Subconscious Mind

What Is Hypnosis ?

Our minds essentially operate at two levels, the "conscious mind" and the "subconscious mind." Our conscious mind is the analytical and/or task oriented part of us. Our subconscious mind contains emotions, habits, and perceptions. The subconscious mind directs how we perceive and relate to the world around us. For effective long-term change to take place we must implement change at the subconscious level. Hypnosis is simply a way to speak directly to the subconscious mind.

How Does Hypnosis Work?

By making positive and **ACCEPTABLE** suggestions directly to the subconscious mind at a time when the client or patient truly wants those changes to take place we can facilitate wonderful changes with relative ease! This is so because the subconscious mind doesn't have the capability to analyze anything. It simply likes an idea or it does not. If it likes the idea it will attach itself to that idea.

Dispelling Misconceptions

What images form in the mind of most people when they think about hypnosis? A mad professor spinning a pinwheel in front of their eyes, a magician swinging a pendant, or maybe count Dracula, with images of bats gleaming in his eyes commanding you to drink blood. As silly as these impressions sound, there are many who believe these gross misconceptions and who harbor unfounded fears about hypnosis. Nothing could be farther from the truth than these superstitious beliefs.

Hypnosis is a wonderful tool that can enhance well-being and lead to a happier and more productive life. Contrary to popular belief, the person being hypnotized is always in control. He or she is definitely not "under the power" of the hypnotist or hypnotherapist. In fact, you may actually experience a heightened awareness when in hypnosis.

When hypnotized, a person is not asleep in the conventional sense of the word. In fact the person is always in complete control. Under normal circumstances no one can make a person do, or say, anything in hypnosis that would violate his or her wishes, morals, or principles. If a suggestion were made that was unacceptable or violated their value system, their subconscious mind would simply reject the suggestion. As well, a person in hypnosis can bring himself/herself out of hypnosis if they choose at any time. So be assured, when in hypnosis, no one can make a person run down the road squawking like a chicken. That could only occur if the person has the desire to act silly in the first place (e.g. a volunteer for a stage hypnotist has agreed, in his/her mind, to be part of the entertainment and will therefore cooperate).

[Note: Hypnosis in conjunction with sensory deprivation, mind altering drugs, etc. can be used in brainwashing and mind control. In stating that under normal circumstances the person cannot be made to do things that would violate their value system, I am not including these extraordinary situations. There are exceptions to this rule.]

CAN HYPNOTHERAPY HELP EVERYONE?

Hypnosis is not a magic bullet. A person who does not want to make changes cannot be forced to change with hypnosis. For example, if a person wants to stop smoking but has been unable to do so on his or her own, hypnosis can help them achieve their goal. If a person is coming to stop smoking because a spouse or friend nagged them into coming, success is unlikely. If, however, a person has a true desire to make positive change in his or her life, the answer is YES, hypnosis can help. The added advantage with hypnosis is that changes made at the subconscious level are more durable and long lasting.

THE POWER OF THE MIND

Those of us who have been involved in hypnotherapy, health and fitness, the martial arts, and/or any ancient or modern healing art, know how incredibly powerful the mind is. A person's perception, mental attitude, faith, and confidence often mean the difference between victory and defeat, health and sickness, and sometimes, life and death. We have all heard about, “the Will to Live” and its positive effect on recovery from illness or injury. An "I can" attitude can be the deciding factor between achieving great success, or succumbing to failure. You can see this occurring everyday of our lives. People with the confidence and faith in themselves and a willingness to test their limits, are the ones that accomplish great things. The most successful people are usually those who have a positive self-image and who view mistakes, obstacles, and setbacks as learning experiences rather than failures. Everything is a positive if you choose to perceive it in that way. Likewise, negative thoughts will become a self-fulfilling prophecy. Look at it this way... if they can sell fertilizer made from horse crap, something of value can be made out of pretty much anything. It's all about perception.

Hypnosis/hypnotherapy is an incredibly powerful tool that can help to unlock your mind's great abilities and potential. While in hypnosis, we utilize much more of our mind's potential than we do in a normal waking state. Generally, however, the public has a skewed perception of what hypnosis is… and if not a skewed perception, at least a very limited one. People sometime view hypnosis as hocus pocus, equating it with the movie image of Dracula commanding his victims to go out like zombies and drink blood. As well, they may equate all hypnosis with the antics of the stage hypnotist. Both perceptions are a far cry from the reality of therapeutic hypnosis. There are truly incredible benefits available through the use of hypnosis.

When hypnosis is mentioned in a clinical context, most people associate it only with things like hypnosis for smoke cessation and for weight loss, but these areas only scratch the surface of what hypnotherapy can accomplish. Hypnosis can be used to modify perception and behavior in a multitude of areas. As a hypnotherapist, some areas where I have been able to help people improve their quality of life include: smoke cessation, weight loss, stress management, pain management, goal achievement (athletic, school grades, professional, etc), overcoming sexual dysfunction, overcoming anxiety, tapping into inner creativity, developing intuitive powers, improving relationships, overcoming fears, improving memory, gaining greater self-esteem and appreciation, breaking negative habits, modifying behaviors, enhancing performance, regression therapy and memory retrieval, and much more. There are ways too numerous to mention through which hypnotherapy can be of benefit. The benefits and possibilities are simply limitless.

HYPNOSIS

Hypnosis is a wonderful and powerful tool in the hands of a skilled hypnotherapist. Basically, here is how it works. As previously stated, the human mind operates essentially at two levels, the conscious mind, and the subconscious mind. Hypnosis is simply a method to get the conscious mind to step aside (temporarily) so that we can speak directly to the subconscious mind, without conscious and/or analytical interference. When this is accomplished, a heightened state of suggestibility is created.

Your conscious mind has four primary functions:

1. It is the analytical part of your mind (In other words, a task oriented problem solver).
2. It is the rational part of your mind (It tries to attach a reason to why things happen).
3. You draw "Will Power" from your conscious mind. (Will power, however, only provides a short burst of determination and is not a long-term solution.)
4. It holds your temporary or short-term memory.

Your Subconscious Mind represents who and what you are. It houses the following:

1. Habits - (Good, bad, and utility)
    Good Habits - Are those that are productive.
    Bad Habits - Are those that are destructive (smoking, compulsive eating, etc.)

Utility Habits - (Automatically closing the door Behind you, covering your mouth when you sneeze, etc.)

2. Emotions – How we feel about circumstances, things, and people.

3. Long term or permanent memory – The permanent recorded storage of events.

[Note: Some memories become irretrievable at a conscious level but are never lost. They can often be retrieved through hypnosis.]

4. Personality – Those traits that cause us to interact with others and to relate to both others and to circumstances that we encounter in the way that we do

5. Intuition – Our intuitive "sense" of things… Our spiritual and/or metaphysical side

6. Creativity – Our ability to transform our visions, thoughts, and dreams into reality

7. Perception – How we see the world

It is the subconscious mind that allows for long-term positive change to take place

POSITIVE SUGGESTION

The subconscious mind is like the little kid in us. It either likes peas or it does not. It needs no reason. It will accept that which it finds pleasing and will reject what it finds unpleasant. By making "POSITIVE," "ACCEPTABLE" suggestions to the subconscious mind at a time when the client truly wants those changes to take place, change can be implemented rapidly. Hypnosis requires two things. One is a competent hypnotherapist. The other is a client who is ready and willing to make positive change in his or her life. It is a team effort between hypnotherapist and client.

CLIENT MISCONCEPTIONS

Hypnosis is probably one of the most misunderstood professions in the world. The movie image and the reality are far different. When hypnotized, people often think it will be as if they are asleep. They are often surprised to find out that they may hear everything that the hypnotherapist says as well as other things that are going on around them (dog barking, noise in another room, etc.). They often think that moving their body or speaking will bring them out of hypnosis. If this were so every stage hypnotist in the world would be out of business. Who would pay to see people sitting in chairs as if they were asleep.

Another common misconception about hypnosis is that a person can be made to do things that you would not willingly do while in hypnosis. Although this is pure fiction, it is a common fear of new clients and patients. It is important to educate new clients or patients about hypnosis. It is essential that all fear be eradicated before proceeding with an induction because fear is the primary ingredient that will prevent the person from going into hypnosis. Remember, hypnosis is a team effort. The hypnotist or hypnotherapist can facilitate the hypnotic state but the client or patient must willingly allow hypnosis to occur.

STAGE HYPNOSIS

Clients, patients, and students often ask me how stage hypnotists get people to do silly things. I tell them quite simply it is because they want to! These people want to be part of the entertainment.

Picture a crowd in a nightclub or theatre watching a stage hypnotist. Often many of the people have had a few drinks, and even if this is not so, all are in a festive mood. The stage hypnotist does not select subjects. He or she will ask for volunteers. Those people that raise their hands and "volunteer" are "agreeing" to be part of the entertainment (even if it makes them look silly). The people who most often volunteer are usually the same people who are the "Life of the Party," or a "Class Clown," even when not in hypnosis. They enjoy being the center of attention and part of the entertainment. The hypnotist will then discretely test the volunteers for suggestibility and compliance under some pretext of part of the show. The most compliant subjects will be kept on stage. The others will be dismissed. The result is that only those people who have the highest desire to cooperate with the stage hypnotist are left on stage. If a person acted silly while in hypnosis as part of a stage show were to come to a hypnotherapist for behavior modification the next day, the therapist would likely have no success in getting that client to do something silly during his or her therapeutic session. It simply would not fit with what that person had come for on that visit and the person's subconscious mind would simply dismiss such suggestions.

THE INTERACTION OF MIND, BODY, AND SPIRIT

In western culture, we have been taught to label our mind, body, and spirit, as if they were three separate creatures. The fact is that when we are centered and balanced they are one… working in harmony. This is easy to see in your daily life. When you are dressed up and looking good, you generally feel better and have a more positive attitude and self image. The condition of your body is directly reflected in your mental state. As well, people who are generally depressed or otherwise negative in their outlook on life, usually have a greater incident of illness. The body responds directly to our state of mind. When you have a strong and healthy, and centered spirit, you also feel great pride (mind), and you may actually carry yourself more proudly (your body). These three elements are not separate. They, in fact, form the whole. They are all properties of one single entity. Together, they are what and who we are. For this reason it is important to incorporate all aspects of mind, body, and spirit, into hypnotherapy sessions.

When we understand the interrelationship between these elements it becomes easy to see the benefit of viewing mind, body, and spirit, as individual properties of one entity. Hypnotherapy can help to reintegrate the parts of the whole. Your powerful subconscious mind has the ability to improve learning and retention, improve focus and enhance coordination. It can increase your confidence. It can reduce pain from injuries and help to expedite the healing of injuries. Your subconscious mind can give you the power to accomplish amazing things in your life.

WHO CAN BENEFIT FROM HYPNOSIS

Anyone with a true desire to make positive change in his/her life can benefit from hypnosis/hypnotherapy. As well, changes made at the subconscious level are more durable and long lasting than those made on a conscious level. Hypnosis is exceptionally good for helping athletes, business people, and artists overcome barriers and maximize their potential.

Hypnosis can be used to weed out distracting thoughts and to eliminate fears. It can help a client or patient to gain focus.

Since learning is a property of the mind, you have a greater chance of achieving anything you can clearly visualize or accept as possible. Hypnosis can help people to more clearly visualize what they want to accomplish. While physical activity trains reflexes and can add muscle tone, it is the mental aspect of our being that will enable one to achieve perfection of form. It is the mind that will determine when, where, and how to use the attributes that we have gained physically. It is the spirit that gives us the determination to do so.

WE CREATE OUR OWN BARRIERS

People generally create their own walls and barriers. Through hypnotherapy, those barriers, anxieties and fears can be brought down. When we are unsure if we can, often we don't. When self-imposed barriers are torn down and replaced with positive thoughts, the person can put all of their energy and focus into accomplishing their goals.

What the mind perceives as real is real to the mind. What we expect to happen usually does. Hypnotherapy can be a rewarding profession. It can help people tear down mental barriers to success, increase confidence and self esteem and maximize their potential. The mind has incredible power. You need only tap into that power to realize dramatic growth and positive change.

Chapter 2

A Brief History of Hypnosis

Hypnosis has been a part of the lives of people since before recorded history. It has been called by many names, although at times remaining nameless cloaked within the ceremonies and rituals of many ancient cultures. Often the seemingly incredible feats performed in ritual were just a product of the not yet understood phenomenon of what we now call hypnotism. Even though the term hypnosis had not yet been created, documentation of hypnotic technique can be found in writings of the ancient Egyptians and Greeks. The oldest written record of the use of hypnotic technique comes from the Ebers Papyrus which provides us with a glimpse into the practice of Egyptian medicine prior to 1552 B.C. It is believed that the Egyptians originated "Sleep - Temples," where priests provided treatment to their followers through the use of "hypnotic suggestion". Hypocrites makes reference to hypnosis, and it seems the Romans learned from the Greeks the value of "trance". In fact, hypnosis has been a key component of virtually every culture and religion known to man.

The rise of Christianity resulted in a decline in the spread of knowledge regarding hypnosis. Misunderstood, hypnosis was equated with witchcraft and spirit worship. Although practiced world wide under many aliases, it would not be until around the 1700's that the study of hypnosis would begin to grow as an area of scientific study.

Key Figures in the History of Hypnosis

Friedrich Anton Mesmer is credited by most as pioneering some of the early scientific study of relaxation techniques and applied suggestion. It is generally thought, however, that he did not fully understand the significance of his research. It is from his name that the term "mesmerism" came.

The **Marquis de Puysegur** was responsible for labeling the three properties of Hypnosis; 1) concentration of the senses on the operator, 2) acceptance of suggestion without question 3) amnesia for events in a trance.

James Braid coined the term "hypnosis in 1842. The word hypnosis came from the Greek word "hypnos" meaning sleep. By the time Braid discovered that hypnosis was not sleep, the term had already caught on.

James Esdaile, was a physician of the early 1800's pioneered the scientific use of hypnosis as an anesthetic for surgery. He performed more surgeries than perhaps anyone before or since using hypnosis for pain management. It was he who identified the depth of trance we now call the Coma or Esdaile State.

Dr. Ambroise-Auguste Liebeault , is regarded by many as the father of modern hypnotism. He concluded that all phenomena related to the hypnotic state are subjective in nature. Liebeault realized that deep levels of hypnosis were not essential for most therapies involving hypnosis. In recognition of this, he was able to develop and utilize methods of what we now refer to as "rapid induction."

In 1880, **Josef Breuer** discovered that through regression, and the recalling of the traumatic experiences from the past, troublesome fears, attitudes, etc. could be alleviated. Prior to Breuer, hypnosis had been used mostly for pain management. This had a profound effect on the growth of the science of hypnotherapy and on the development of what became known as "psychoanalysis."

My personal choice for the father of modern hypnotherapy is **David Elman**. When Elman was eight, his father was suffering from terminal cancer. Elman witnessed a visiting stage hypnotist alleviate his father's pain through the use of hypnosis. Elman never forgot this. Elman himself worked for a short time as a stage hypnotist. It was during this time that he developed rapid induction techniques that brought him recognition.

Elman believed in keeping it simple. During the 1950's it was Elman, possibly more than anyone, who brought to light the importance of semantics used by the hypnotist/hypnotherapist, and the role of expectancy on the part of the subject. His depth of understanding of the properties of the conscious and subconscious mind laid the groundwork for many of the techniques used by hypnotherapists around the world to this day.

Chapter 3

WHAT YOU NEED FOR HYPNOSIS (Compliance / Expectation / Motivation)

COMPLIANCE

It is essential that your client or patient be willing to follow your instructions without fear or reservation. After the intake and pre-talk and before inducing hypnosis, I make it a point to ask the subject for their commitment to follow my instructions. If they say, "I'll try," I reply something like this, "That's not good enough. Try is the disciple of defeat. Try gives you a back door out. You can tell yourself that you didn't say you would do it. You just said that you would try. We need more than that. I need your commitment that you will follow my instructions at all times. So, if I ask you to imagine that you've got moose antlers and webbed feet, you're going to do it, right!" When the client/patient agrees, we proceed.

Compliance is essential. If you have done your pre-talk properly, the client/patient will be prepared to make that commitment. In the pre-talk, you must establish trust and rapport and eliminat their fears. They must also be aware that you will always work in their best interest and that you will always keep them safe and secure. Without compliance, you will not get far with the therapy.

EXPECTATION

What the mind expects to happen usually happens. If a person expects success they will likely achieve it. Conversely, if he or she has doubts about their chances for success, they are doomed to failure. With hypnosis and hypnotherapy you are talking to the child within the person. If you create a pleasant and appealing picture and establish positive thought patterns (the feeling that the person can in fact achieve their goal), the person will likely accomplish what he or she expects to accomplish. As a hypnotist or hypnotherapist, you are also an inspirational motivator and a life coach. It is your job to help the client believe in him or herself. This must be accomplished BEFORE hypnosis is induced. That "waking hypnotic suggestion," prior to the induction, will make your job within the session easier by far.

RESISTANCE

Erickson said, "there is no resistance, just a lack of rapport" (or something to that effect). This is very true. If the client or patient is properly prepared, there will be no resistance. This means that they must trust you, they must be fear free, they must be willing to let go of the need to control and allow you to do your work.

Resistance is usually the product of fear, the need to control, a misconception about what role they themselves play in the hypnotic process, or a misunderstanding of what they might experience in hypnosis. Any combination of these factors will prevent success. It is important to educate the person about the hypnotic process. They must understand that one cannot "try" to be hypnotized. Let them know that if they simply relax and enjoy, you can do your job and they can easily accomplish their goal. Most people are surprised when I tell them that they don't have to "listen" to me. Let your client or patient know that if they hear you or if they don't hear you it's fine either way. Let them know that if thoughts or images drift through their mind that's fine too. What is important is that they don't try to bring thoughts in, or push them out. I suggest that they just let any thoughts that pass through their mind process naturally.

When working with a client or patient with a controlling personality I will often stop the intake momentarily and tell them something like this. "Listen NAME, if you don't want to follow my suggestions completely, you can do that. You always have the power… its up to you. But if that's your choice, my wife and I will have a great steak dinner on your fee, and you won't accomplish your goal. On the other hand, if you want to accomplish what you've come here for, then trust me, and let me do the work you've paid me to do." This approach has worked well for me on more occasions than I can count. Each situation is different but what remains constant is that you must have a subject who is willing to let you do your work.

WHAT WILL PREVENT HYPNOSIS

The number one thing that will prevent hypnosis is fear. Alleviating fear must be done in the pre-talk. The number two thing that will prevent hypnosis is the person "trying." You must assure the client that hypnosis is a naturally occurring phenomenon. Explain that they can best succeed by not trying. Trying is a product of the conscious mind. Since a hypnotic induction is a process intended to get the conscious mind to step aside it stands to reason that we don't want the client to do anything that would entice the conscious mind back into play.

MOTIVATION AND INDIVIDUAL PERCEPTION

Virtually every person uses the same basic perceptual tools to define his or her world. Most people (extraordinary perceptual senses aside) have the ability to smell, taste, see, touch, and hear. It is important to remember, however, that we all process the information that we take in through these senses very differently. This is why some people find the taste of asparagus pleasing and others find it disgusting. As well, people prioritize that information differently. To some people, sight is the most significant of the senses. To others it may be sound, touch, taste, or smell. When you include the various combinations in which these senses can be prioritized it is a simple matter to see why each individual will perceive the world in a different way.

Visualization to the hypnotherapist should represent more than merely visual sensory perception. It represents a total picture developed by use of all the senses working in concert to create each person's unique perception of life. In using all of the senses, "visualizations" become far more significant, meaningful, vivid and therefore more useful.

INDIVIDUAL SIGNIFICANCE

When creating "visualizations," it is most helpful to find out what senses are most significant to that particular person. As well, it is important to know how that person prioritizes the stimuli that he or she takes in. The method that I use is simple.

During the intake process, I determine the therapeutic approach that I will use within the session. Especially when I plan to use visualization to any significant degree, I first conduct a simple test to find out which sensory perception will be most useful with that particular person.

First, I help the person gain confidence in his or her ability to visualize. I offer encouragement by telling the person that I know that he or she has a great imagination. I say something (to adults in particular), like this… "After all John, you know that we never lose that great imagination that we had as kids. We simply layer over it with the stuff we pick up on the way to adulthood. You still have the same great imagination you had when you used to play Cowboys and Indians (or whatever) as a kid." I then encourage the person to tap into that great imagination. I ask them to close their eyes. I tell them that I want them to practice using that great imagination by visualizing anything that I mention to them. I explain that I will be giving them all sorts of sights, sounds, smells, tastes, and touch sensations that I would like them to create with their wonderful imagination. I then begin to move through the five senses offering sensations that I would like them to imagine. For example I might say, "I'd like you to imagine the sight of a bright red beach ball and when you have it clearly in your mind, let me know." When they say they have it, I give them another object to visualize each becoming slightly more complex than the last. I might say for the next object, "Imagine the sight of a flag blowing in the wind." When he or she has it, we move on to the next visualization. I will do this with five or six different objects.

I then move to another sense. I might say, "Now I would like you to imagine the smell of the inside of a flower shop." When they have it, I move on to another smell and then another. I repeat this process for all five senses.

When I have concluded these visualizations, I ask the person to share with me which of their five senses was the most vivid for them. As well, I ask which sense was second strongest, third, fourth, and fifth strongest. I list these in their order of strength (for my future reference). Although I may use all of the five senses within the visualizations I suggest, or during an induction, I will focus primarily on the top two or three. In other words, the visualization properties that are strongest to that individual are the ones that I will incorporate. The only time that I will not use all of the senses is if the person simply had very little or no impression for one of the senses. At the same time, I will note the amount of time that it took for the person to visualize within each category and to respond that he or she had completed that visualization successfully. If a person were able to quickly develop visualizations in the smell category but took much longer to develop visualizations involving sound, I would factor that information into my hierarchy of senses during the actual session visualizations. This would be so regardless of the priority order list that I had developed by questioning the person. This information is significant because I want to create visualizations as quickly and easily as possible during the therapeutic session.

WHY VISUALIZATIONS

Hypnosis is simply a device to get the conscious mind to step aside so that the hypnotherapist can speak directly to the subconscious mind. Visualizations can be a valuable tool in keeping the conscious mind on the sidelines.

I begin prepping people for proficiency in visualization early in the pre-talk. I subtly give them "permission" to let their mind, wander float and dream while enjoying the wonderful feeling of hypnosis. I give the person permission, NOT to listen to me. I often create the following analogy (or something similar): I'll say, "Have you ever been relaxing on the beach with dozens of people all around you. The person next to you might have been talking, but you were so wonderfully relaxed and off in your own world, that everything else seemed to be miles away. If someone were to ask you what the person next to you just said, you probably couldn't tell them... right! That same feeling may very well happen with you today and if it does, and you drift off and lose track of my voice, that's okay. Don't be concerned or attempt to refocus on my words. There is no need. Your powerful subconscious mind will always hear me. You can simply continue to enjoy your day at the beach." Furthermore, as a hypnotic suggestion, I will often include, "You may chose to listen to my voice or you may chose not to listen to my voice. It really doesn't matter. Your powerful subconscious mind will always hear me." The client or patient now has permission, and the freedom to simply relax and enjoy.

Visualization can be a powerful tool to help your clients enjoy hypnosis. Even when using something as rudimentary as simple direct suggestion as your primary tool, a meaningful visualization is an easy way to deepen or to maintain depth of trance. I find out what activity, place, or thing, the person enjoys. Then I take them there. I keep my suggestions simple and broad. This leaves the creative process completely up to the individual. The person gets exactly what he or she wants because for the most part they developed the visualization by themselves. If the person is not particularly visual, you can simply change your phrasing to, "Imagine" or "What If." Virtually anyone can work with that. Then I give them permission to "stay and enjoy" that place while I help them accomplish their goal. I will usually say something like this. "Stay and enjoy this wonderful feeling. Nothing else matters, this is your special time. Don't be concerned with me. Simply enjoy! Your powerful subconscious mind will always hear me."

When creating the visualization I use the sights, smells, sounds, tastes, and feels (temperature, skin sensations, etc.) that he or she would normally be experiencing, in the place of their choice, prioritized via the information collected during the intake. While the person relaxes and enjoys the wonderful place that we have chosen,

I make the necessary suggestions to help them accomplish their goal.

IMPORTANCE OF USING ALL OF THE SENSES

To one degree or another, I use visualization in a significant percentage of my session work. This is so even within the context of using simple "direct suggestion." Using all of the senses in visualization can be of even greater value when using indirect or other metaphoric methods of suggestion. The usefulness of visualization is not restricted to only those times when visualization is the primary therapeutic vehicle. Using all of the senses accomplishes two things. (1) It makes the visualization more vivid. (2) It helps to maintain the level or depth of trance. This is especially true when dealing with a person that might otherwise allow the conscious mind to try and "sneak a peek." The more vivid and pleasant the visualization grows, the more stable the depth of trance will become. The conscious mind will have stepped totally out of the picture allowing the subconscious mind to lock firmly onto your suggestions.

BOTTOM LINE

The most powerful visualizations incorporate all of the senses. Using all of the senses, however, is not enough. You must know which senses are the most powerful to that individual. Only then can you make the most of the information you have gathered. This information will give power in deepening the level of trance as well as in maintaining a stable depth of trance. Your suggestions will be adhered to more powerfully providing your client with better results and you with a higher success record.

THE POWER OF WORDS

Ask someone you know to describe something very powerful to you. In fact, ask ten or twenty people. You'll get a variety of answers but most will be things like, a hurricane, tornados, an atomic bomb, or a speeding locomotive. I'll bet no one will offer the answer "words." The fact is that words are the most powerful thing in the world. Virtually everything that we know about life and our world has been imparted to us through words. Our ideas, perceptions, and beliefs, have all been generated through our perception of words. They may have been spoken, signed, or written words, but our knowledge of the universe is in fact a product of our understanding of words and what those words mean to each of us.

If you were raising a child and told that child to "look at the pretty red grass" or "look at the bright green sky," his or her perception of green and red and the connection between the actual color and the word representing it would be vastly different than yours or mine. Likewise, the words that we use each day (and take for granted) often represent very different meanings and perceptions to each of us. A student of mine, originally from India, once told me that the hardest thing for him in learning the English language was learning to "think in English." This illustrates how powerful words are and why semantics are so incredibly important in hypnotherapy. In fact, I would say semantics is the most important part of therapeutic hypnosis.

A short time ago I was in session with a gentleman discussing the importance of self-talk. His self-esteem issues were in great part exacerbated by his tendency toward perpetual negative self-talk. Before our sessions he had never recognized his tendency for negative self-talk. After our discussion he looked at me and said, "You know Doc, I never thought about it that way before. Words are really important.

You're the first person who ever said that to me. I guess that makes you a 'Doctor of Words'." I reflected on his statement for a moment thinking how profound it really was. A skilled hypnotherapist is in a sense a "Master of Words."

We all realize how powerful the words of an adult can be to a child. To the child adults are powerful giants. Our words, no matter how insignificant to an adult, make a lasting impression on the child. That is why it is so important to speak to children in positive and reinforcing terms. If you bombard a child with negative talk or tell a child that he or she is a failure, bad, or incompetent, the child will probably live up to your negative expectations. If you tell a child that he or she "can do it," or how beautifully the child draws, or sings, how much you love them, or what a good person he or she is, the child will probably live up to that expectation. The same holds true when adults say things to each other. Many times in your life I am sure you have experienced the power of words. They can affect us emotionally… even physically. When a person tells you something complimentary, it makes you feel great, right down to the tips of your toes. You may get butterflies in your stomach, get a warm tingly feeling, or it may even bring a tear of joy to your eyes. By the same token, if someone says something hurtful to you, you will feel that as well. Sometimes these powerful emotions may even cause physical discomfort. Your heart may race, you may get a hot flash, or a knot in your stomach. Why then do we assume that self-talk is any less powerful than the words that others say to us? When working with self-esteem issues I frequently focus on creating positive self-talk within the person. This continuing and repetitive positive self-talk results in benefits from the waking hypnotic suggestion created. This waking hypnotic suggestion is further compounded each and every time that positive self-talk takes place.

SEMANTICS

It is critically important in successful hypnotherapy to use our words wisely and to recognize that others may not perceive words in the same way that you do. The information that you need to avoid those pitfalls should be acquired in the intake. As an example, if you suggest to your client a visualization where the person is on the beach in the warm sun, and the person happens to hate the beach or gets sunburned easily, you are going to miss the boat with that person. You may love the beach. If your client does not, that visualization will be worse than useless. Suggesting that this person feel the warmth of the sun could have the same effect as suggesting that you will enjoy a Popsicle stick up your nose.

A while back, at one of our classes here at Master's Center Institute of Hypnotherapy, I was teaching the Elman Induction. Each student was demonstrating his or her skills in preparing the would-be client for the induction. One of my students was teaching his classmate to hold relaxation in her eyelids (the eye-lock portion of the induction prep). His phrasing to her went something like this… " I want you to relax your eyes very deeply. In a moment I'm going to ask you to try and open them and when you do, you'll find out that your eyes don't work." MAN, WHAT A SCARY THOUGHT THAT IS! He knew what he meant but that statement could sound scary to anyone else… especially to a person with no knowledge of hypnosis.

There is a delicate balance in keeping our words evoking and meaningful, and at the same time keeping them benign. The phrase that I use with my students is that we need to give the client or patient the brush, but let him or her paint the picture. A competent therapist uses words that allow the person to develop his or her own perception and images of the words the therapist uses. Below are some examples of phrasing that I would, and would not use.

Would Not Use: You are on the beach (or wherever) or, You feel warm (cool, etc.).

Would Use: What if you were at (Location that you know the person likes, e.g.: the beach or park) on a comfortable and pleasant day.

Reason: If you tell someone that they are experiencing something and they are not, they will feel that either you, or they, have failed. If this occurs the session will most likely be ineffective. "What if you were," or "imagine yourself," will give the person the ability to generate their unique perception of your words.

Would Not Use: You feel perfectly comfortable

Would Use: Notice how you can grow more peaceful and calm with each and every breath you exhale.

Reason: Again, if you tell someone that they are experiencing something and they are not, they may feel that either you, or they, have failed. If this occurs the session will suffer.

Would Not Use: Cigarettes are killing you (e.g. smoke cessation).

Would Use: Your body has already begun the healing process. Greater health and vitality are now yours as a non-smoker.

Reason: The subconscious mind does not attach well to negative suggestion. Always focus on the positive. As well, I speak in terms that suggest success has already been achieved (e.g.: are now yours as a non-smoker).

Before using words such as "deeper", I pre-qualify what the word(s) will mean. This is done during the intake and pre-talk. A word like deeper may feel perfectly safe to one person while creating fearful images to another. To one person going deeper may elicit images of drifting gently on the waves at the beach, while to someone who has previously been trapped in a basement or cave that same word may evoke fear or at least uneasiness. You can never be certain how a particular word will affect any one individual. Care in gathering data during the intake will help you in choosing the right words for your client or patient.

YOUR WORDS

Each hypnotherapist and/or student needs to be aware of his or her use of semantics. One way to do this is to audiotape sessions in order to critique yourself. After making a tape put it away for a week or two. Then listen to it with fresh ears. Look for how your words may sound differently than you intended them to, or if they have multiple meanings that the client may misinterpret. You may be surprised at what you hear.

Words are the delicate surgical tools that we as hypnotherapists use to remove the tumors of doubt, insecurity, fear, and negativity. They must be wielded with the same care as that of a neurosurgeon's scalpel. While a surgeon works with the tissue of the body, we work with that part of an individual that is the essence of who they are. This obligation should never be taken lightly.

Chapter 4
Hypnotherapeutic Methods

METHODS

Within the field of hypnotherapy there are three primary methods or tools with which the hypnotist or hypnotherapist helps their clients or patients achieve their goals. The methods or tools generally used are, "direct suggestion", "indirect suggestion", and "regression". Each is equally important. A competent hypnotist or hypnotherapist knows how to use the proper tool in the appropriate circumstance. Below is outlined what each of the methods mentioned represents.

DIRECT SUGGESTION:

Direct suggestion is exactly what it implies. A suggestion is made while the subject is in hypnosis. If in fact the subconscious finds the suggestion acceptable, it will simply attach to it thereby facilitating the desired change in perception and behavior. An example of direct suggestion would be, "You are now a non-smoker and you will remain a non-smoker for the rest of your life".

INDIRECT SUGGESTION:

Indirect suggestion is metaphoric. As an example, a boy in his early teens was brought to me for a social phobia. It so happened that he loved soccer. Because of his love for soccer I simply built his entire session around a game of soccer. Within this game he was able to address and conquer his fears. Indirect suggestion can be in the form of an analogy, an association (e.g.: you feel free as a bird), or a story or fable where the story exemplifies the goal of that person.

REGRESSION:

Regression is a technique whereby the person is induced to drift back through time and either vividly remember (hypermnesia), or relive (true regression), moments or events that originally developed the perceptions and/or emotions that are the root cause of the client/patient's problem. [Note: Abreaction, or the experiencing and working through troublesome emotions is often a part of the therapeutic approach within a regression session.]

LESS IS MORE

The most frequent problem I have seen with inexperienced hypnotherapists is the urge to do more than is necessary. For example, most hypnotists and hypnotherapists find regression therapy to be very interesting. I admit that regression is the method that I most like to work with. It can be extremely interesting… for me. The fact remains though that it doesn't make sense to hunt a squirrel with an elephant gun. We should not be working with clients or patients for our own amusement. A quality therapist seeks to help his or her client reach their goal in the shortest possible of time. For this reason… Less is more, so "Keep it Simple." Direct Suggestion is by far the simplest approach.

Ninety-nine times out of a hundred, direct suggestion is the most efficient way to accomplish the client's goal. That doesn't mean that indirect suggestion or perhaps regression therapy wouldn't work in those cases. It simply means that there is no practical or ethical reason to take the long way around the block. If the subconscious mind is prepared to modify perception based on a simple direct suggestion, then that is the best approach. Unless I am convinced during the intake that the only way I can help the person is with regression, I will always implement direct suggestion first. If I am not getting the results I want with the direct suggestion, then and only then will I move to indirect suggestion or regression therapy.

REGRESSION THERAPY CLIENT PRECONCEPTIONS

We, as professionals in the field of hypnotherapy, are well acquainted with the terms and tools of our profession. Due to our comfort level based on our knowledge of hypnosis and hypnotherapy it is easy for many of us to overlook how others from outside of our profession may perceive those things that we relate to as normal daily activity. Think about those times when you may have contacted technical support for a computer problem or discussed a mechanical problem with your auto mechanic, accountant, or plumber. If those areas are outside of your scope of knowledge, you may very well have felt uneasy with allowing that person to direct your decision. It is important for us to be aware that both the concepts of regression and of hypnosis can conjure up entirely different pictures for the layman than they do for those within our profession.

To illustrate how differently those outside of our practice view hypnosis/hypnotherapy, most of us need only look to those who enter our doors each day. Virtually every one of us (in active practice) has at least one person each week that thinks they will be mystically "under our power" during their session. Where hypnosis is concerned, the general public knows only what they see in the movies (Count Dracula), and in stage shows (people acting foolishly). It should come as no surprise that many prospective clients are apprehensive about hypnotherapy and especially about regression therapy. In virtually every instance on TV and in the movies, people discover horrible and frightening things when regressed. We know that this is not true, but it sells for the entertainment industry. The fact remains, however, that the theatre image is often our client's only point of reference and perception regarding regression.

Regardless of the therapy that will follow, it has always been my view that the intake, consultation, and pre-talk are the most important factors in achieving success with a client. The pre-talk in particular, is the time that you will either create a rapport with your client or lose effectiveness with him or her. The pre-talk is your opportunity to create understanding that will open the door to a successful session(s).

PREPARATION

During my pre-talk with a new client, I create rapport in the following ways. I start by getting to know about them personally. People generally like to talk about themselves, and I encourage that. I ask them if they have any questions or concerns and I address those concerns. [Note: Never use statements like: Do you have any "fears" or "worries" about hypnosis. You may inadvertently cause the person to become worried or fearful. I ask only if they have any concerns or questions.] I take the opportunity to educate them about hypnosis and hypnotherapy. I stress that people experience hypnosis in various ways, and for that reason, they can't do it wrong. This helps them to gain confidence. When regression therapy is indicated, I use this time also to explain what regression is and is not, and how it will be of benefit. As well, I entertain them. I play some hypnosis, visualization, and imagination games/demonstrations to lighten the atmosphere and put the new client at ease. As well, I use that opportunity to assure them that they have the complete ability to be an excellent subject. I give them confidence and create expectation. [Note: By this time, in most cases, I have already induced hypnosis via subtle "hypno-games" or "demonstrations". I do this without ever mentioning the word hypnosis. By the time we get to the actual session… they have already been in hypnosis and they are "super-prepared".]

EDUCATING THE CLIENT ABOUT REGRESSION

Assuming that you have successfully relieved all of your client's concerns about hypnosis in general, you can now move on to creating a positive outlook about regression therapy. The fear that is most often present is the fear of the unknown. The fear that they may confront something uncomfortable or even frightening during regression is common. After all, that's what usually happens on TV. I usually begin by explaining that the therapies that I utilize fall into three main categories: direct suggestion, indirect suggestion, and regression. I explain that when regression therapy is indicated, it can be a very powerful tool to facilitate wonderful and positive change. I ask them… "You want to accomplish your goal, don't you?" Of course they answer with "Yes". I then help the client to have a positive and exciting outlook about regression. I ease any concerns that they may be feeling by saying something to the following effect.

Example:

Today (first visit), we may not even get so far as to pursue your actual therapy. Instead, we'll start by helping you to become more comfortable with the process involved in hypnotherapy. It will also be an opportunity for you to see how really wonderful hypnosis is. Also, you'll be pleasantly surprised to how very powerful your mind actually is. Today will be sort of a "test drive"... you're going to love this. I continue to explain to the client:

In the movies, people undergoing regression generally find out that their mother was from Venus or their father was an evil Troll... right. We all know that this isn't true. This is entertainment, not real life. The fact of the matter is that it is the exception to the rule when people discover something terrible during regression. There is an interesting reason that most problems are a result of circumstances that are not so big. Would you like to hear how that happens? (Client: Yes). Here is an example. I have three children. There are times when one or the other will come to me with tears in their eyes because another child may have said something that hurt their feelings. The first instinct of most adults is to address the problem by telling the child not to let it bother him or her because "it is not really a big deal." As an adult, we know from life experience that in the bigger picture, that specific problem is probably not a big deal. To the child, however, it is a very big deal at that moment. As we grow older we become more resilient to the things that once hurt us as children. We layer over our most basic emotions with coatings of logic and rational thought. The child however is still in us. The point is that instances that can facilitate problems later in life are often small things that seemed big to us at that time (as children). I often use as an example with my clients a case where a woman who came to me with serious self-esteem problems. She had unsuccessfully sought to resolve her problems with psychologists, psychiatrists, and through other forms of counseling. When I suggested regression therapy she immediately said no to my suggestion. She was afraid of what she would uncover. She was certain that something terrible had happened during her childhood. After relieving her fears I did her session. After inducing hypnosis, I asked her to go back in time to the moment that was most significant to her, that precipitated her feeling that she was less than she would like to be. After regressing my client the conversation went something like this (I will edit the conversation keeping to the most relevant items).

Dr. H: Where are you Jane (not her real name), inside or out?
Client: Inside.

Dr. H: Are you alone or are you with someone?

Client: With someone.

Dr. H: Who are you with?

Client: My mother.

Dr. H: I'm curious, would you tell me what is going on?

Client: My mother is yelling at me. She's calling me stupid and telling me I can't do anything right.

Dr. H: My word… Why is she so upset with you? Will you please tell me?

Client: I'm setting the table and making a big mess.

Dr. H: How old are you?

Client: Two

I then explain to the person I am working with that I was able to help this person by simply re-framing the incident that was the catalyst for her low self-esteem. I explain that I suggested that she (the little girl) had nothing to feel guilty about, that in fact she could be proud that she was trying to help despite the fact that her mother reacted inappropriately to her efforts (perhaps just having a bad day). As the subconscious mind accepted my suggestions it started a domino effect that caused wonderful and positive changes to take place regarding her self image and within her entire life. You can use examples like these to alleviate fears by showing clients that our problems do not always come from terrible and traumatic circumstances as we would interpret than by adult standards. They are usually from something that was significant to the inner child and that would not seem so terrible to the adult. But it is true that what the mind perceives to be real is real to the mind and to that child, the event was significant. You can be sure that in regression, it is not the norm to uncover a past encounter with a fiend or space monster. It is more likely to find something that was significant and disturbing to the child that would not be so significant by adult standards.

[Note: The examples are directed to adult clients. The approach is somewhat different when preparing younger people for regression therapy.]

FURTHER PREP

Before beginning a session, I ask clients to tell me about some life experiences that hold especially fond memories for them. After getting this information, I ask them if they would like to re-experience some of those moments. The conversation goes something like this…
Do you want to see something really neat? (Client: yes). How would you like to have that same wonderful feeling again that you had when… (client's experience). This is really

going to be fun. You'd like that wouldn't you? (Client: yes) Watch how easy this is.

Then I begin regression with what I call a practice trip. When the practice trip is completed I have a wonderfully prepared person, acceptant of, and willing to do regression. From this point forward the actual regression session is smooth, easy, and effective.

RESULTS

It may seem like a lot of work to go through. Actually this whole process doesn't take long if you know where you are going with it ahead of time. In the end, I find that taking this little bit of additional time at the beginning actually saves time over the long run and provides better results. Remember too, this only needs to be done on the first session. By systematically creating rapport and a trust, alleviating fear, creating an atmosphere of fun and anticipation, and by allowing the person to "practice" regression in a non-threatening way, you will drastically improve your success rate. You will gain a loyal and grateful client who will sing your praises, and as we all know… word of mouth is the best advertisement.

DEEPENING AND PERCEPTION

In hypnosis and hypnotherapy we frequently hear the phrase "go deeper." Too often therapists don't stop to think about what the phrase "***Go Deeper***" means to the client or patient they are working with. Perception about virtually everything in the world is different from person to person. That's why two people can see the same movie, hear the same conversation, or see the same event, and get something totally different out of it. We all perceive the world differently based on our life experience.

DEEPER

Every client/patient has his or her unique perception about what the term deeper means. You can use that to your advantage in session. Here is what I do during the pre-talk and intake. This might be of value to you in helping those you work with more quickly achieve somnambulism thereby leading to more efficient use of your time and a more productive session.

During the intake I ask the person to close his or her eyes for a moment. When their eyes are closed I encourage them to relax with a couple of deep breaths. I tell them that in a moment I will say something to them and that when I do, I want them to create an image or perception in their mind that is both safe and secure that meets their perception of what I say. I tell them that each time I say the phrase I would like them to allow that image to become more vivid to them. I pause for a moment and then I say, "Now, go deeper into relaxation." I repeat to the person "Now drift even deeper, just let yourself go deeper into relaxation." "Feel yourself "drifting deeper." "Imagine yourself going deeper," and so on. I always stress the word "deeper." After a few repetitions of this I have the person open their eyes and I immediately ask the person, "What images, feelings, or sensations, did going deeper into relaxation create for you. What was your perception of going deeper?" You will be surprised at the number of useful visualizations and perceptions that your clients or patients will respond with.

SIGNIFICANCE

Any image or perception that is significant to your client or patient will be far more powerful than one that you might create for the person. You can simply take the person's perception of "DEEPER" and use that perception to quickly and easily deepen the person's hypnotic state. This saves time and effort for you. It also assures that the person will be relating to your words in a way that is meaningful, safe, and secure for them. Try it… You'll like it!

Chapter 5

What is an Induction?

An induction is a tool or mechanism used to induce a state of hypnosis. It is a strategy with which to get the conscious mind to step aside in order to have direct access to the subconscious mind. There are many forms of inductions.

Some of the more common inductions are:

1. **Progressive Relaxation:** A systematic relaxation of the body progressing from the head to the toes (or vice versa) accompanied with suggestions and/or visualizations that help to further deepen that state of relaxation. The progression of relaxation is usually repeated multiple times until high levels of physical relaxation generate the mental relaxation needed for trance.

2. **Ericksonian:** A form of hypnosis that utilizes both metaphor, and a relating back to the subjects the physical signs of relaxation that are occurring. (E.g.: "And I notice that as your breathing becomes more gentle and slow that you drift deeper into relaxation."

3. **Rapid and Instant:** There are two primary ways to inspire the conscious mind to step aside so that we can have clear access to the subconscious mind. One is to bore the conscious mind out of the way (as with Ericksonian and progressive relaxation techniques). The other is to startle it out of the way. This is accomplished by providing an instant, intense distraction to the conscious mind. At the moment this happens there is a brief window of opportunity for suggestion to relax, or sleep, that may be capitalized on to facilitate

trance (even though we know that hypnosis is not sleep, for most people the idea of sleep fits).

Rapid and instant inductions use a variety of techniques (startling the conscious mind out of the way, boring the conscious mind out of the way, confusing the conscious mind out of the way, etc.) to facilitate hypnosis. Instant inductions facilitate hypnosis instantly (as one might suspect) or at least within seconds. Rapid inductions will generally take from three to six minutes.

4. **Fixation:** Fixation uses an object (pendulum), a light, or some other focal point to tire the eyes. Fixation also works with the principle of boring the conscious mind out of the way.

5: **Confusion:** Confusion inductions overload the conscious mind with input. The conscious mind seeks escape and steps aside.

Induction and Therapeutic Approaches:

In using the above inductions it is important to take into consideration the two primary approaches in administering an induction or in making suggestion. The two are as follows.

1. **Authoritarian (Paternal):** The hypnotist or hypnotherapist takes an assertive role in the induction and in the subsequent therapeutic process. This usually represents more than simply pacing and leading. The therapist directs to a greater degree the content and pace of the session.

2. **Maternal**: Maternal inductions and therapies are nurturing and gentle. They are more soothing in nature. I sometimes equate the difference between maternal and

authoritarian approaches as being similar to the difference between a gentle massage and a deep tissue massage.

I personally favor authoritarian inductions, and in particular those that would be classified as rapid inductions or instant inductions. Keep in mind that my preference comes from the fact that I have worked for years in clinical practice. In order to see any number of people each day, it is important to work with inductions that are effective and at the same time speedy. If you have only an hour with the client or patient and a portion of that time will be updating client or patient information, it stands to reason that you cannot take a half-hour to induce hypnosis. There would be no time left for the therapy itself. [Note: I allow one and a half to two hours for a first session and forty-five minutes to an hour for follow-up sessions (depending on the nature of the problem).] There are many therapists who still use progressive relaxation and other maternal induction methods. As well, many use maternal therapeutic approaches… I don't. It's the long way around the block. In fact, my least favorite of all inductions is progressive relaxation. It takes too long, and it rarely gets the depth of trance needed for durable suggestion (somnambulism) until after multiple sessions.

I am an advocate of the authoritarian or paternal approach and this is why. When a person comes to you for help it is generally because they are ready to accept help. What better time than this to give the person concrete direction. An authoritarian approach doesn't mean that you boss or command the person. It simply means that you take a more assertive and directive role. If your goal is to move the person from point "A" to point "B" in the shortest possible time, what better way than to direct them when they have already asked for that direction. As with massage, a gentle massage is peaceful, but if you want to get the knots out of those muscles a deep tissue massage is the fastest way to get the job done.

There are exceptions to any rule. Once or twice a year I resort to progressive relaxation when it is appropriate. For example, I had an elderly woman come to me who was quite high-strung and somewhat nervous about the idea of hypnosis. For her, anything other than a maternal approach would not have been appropriate on the initial visit. I wanted her first visit to be very calming in order to increase her comfort level with the process of hypnotherapy. On her first session I used a progressive relaxation technique. On her second session we switched to a rapid induction. By the second session she was significantly more comfortable with hypnosis and more trusting of me as her therapist.

My favorite induction is the Elman Induction. It is quick (about 4 to 5 minutes), it has built in testing, and it generally enables the client or patient to achieve somnambulism on the first session. Below is a sample of the Elman induction.

Sample Use of The Elman Induction Created by Dave Elman

Now “John”… Take a deep breath fill up your lungs and hold it for a second. Now exhale and close your eyes and relax them very deeply. Just let them become loose and warm like that moment between awake and asleep when you drift off at night. Place your awareness on your eyelids, and relax your eyes to the point where they just won't work. And when you know you've relaxed them to the point where they just won't work hold that relaxation right there in your eyes and give them a good test, make sure they won't work, and notice how good that feels. (Subject tests eyes and they remain relaxed. / See companion videotape to this book for complete demonstration of prep and induction.)

Therapist: perfect

Now we can deepen this relaxation even more, notice how easy this is. John, I'd you to take that feeling that your holding in your eyes and move it on up to the top of your head and let that part of your body relax very deeply… excellent

Now take that feeling and send it down from the top of your head right through your body to the tips of your toes, feel it like a warm wave of relaxation as it drifts through your body, just let yourself go more deeply relaxed. Excellent… you're doing Great.

Now we can deepen this physical relaxation even more. Notice how easy this is. I'd like you to use that wonderful imagination that I know you have. That same wonderful imagination that you had as a small child, and I'd like you to imagine now that any surface tension, stress, or irritation you may have picked up in the last day, or week, or month, is just lifting up from your body like a cloud of mist. Feel it lifting and separating from your body, moving away, disappearing like a cloud of mist vanishes in the morning sun, and as it does your body relaxes loose and limp like a rag doll… perfect

Now we can deepen this relaxation even more. I'd like you to use that wonderful imagination of yours again and imagine that you're wrapped in a warm, wonderful blanket of relaxation. Start with the idea of wanting that to happen. You'll see how easily it will happen. Feel that warm wonderful blanket of relaxation around you. Now just let that relaxation soak into your body and let yourself relax much more. terrific!

Now we can deepen this relaxation even more. In a moment John, I'm going to ask you to open and close your eyes. When I ask you to close your eyes, I want you to close them down send another wave of relaxation all the way through your body so that very quickly you allow the physical part of you to relax ten times deeper. Allow your eyes to become open, now close them way down, loose and limp and relax very deeply. Excellent, you're doing great.

Now we can deepen this relaxation even more. In a moment I'm going to have you open and close your eyes again, when I have you close your eyes, close them down send another wave of relaxation all the way through your body and when you do, go ahead and double the relaxation. Allow your eyes to become open, now close them way down, and really let go this time. Perfect your doing great.

Now we can deepen this relaxation even more. In a moment I'm going to ask you to open and close your eyes one more time. When I ask you to close your eyes, close them down, send another wave of relaxation all the way through you body and when you do, go ahead and double that relaxation again. Let it grow even deeper. Allow your eyes to become open now, close them way down. Loose and limp, just relax like a rag doll. Perfect!

Now John, in a moment I'm going to lift your right arm up by the wrist, just a couple of inches. This is just for me to tell if you've been able to follow my suggestions for physical relaxation, because if you have, when I lift that arm, that entire hand and arm will feel to me to be so deeply relaxed that it will feel as if I'm lifting a soaking wet rag, or a piece of stone. It will just be wonderfully and deeply relaxed. Then I'm going to drop that hand back down on your lap. It will plop back down like the arm of a rag-doll. When that happens just let yourself go more deeply relaxed. When I lift that arm, don't help me. Let me do all the lifting. You know you could lift your arm. That would be easy, but in order to do that you would have to remove that great relaxation that you're experiencing and that's not why you came here today. Let me do all the lifting and when that hand plops back down just relax much more… Perfect!

Now we have a wonderful quality of relaxation of the body, let's go ahead and relax that mind, when the mind is relaxed it feels wonderfully calm. Mental relaxation is easy to get; here is how you'll do it. In a moment I'm going to ask you to begin counting backwards slowly, out loud, beginning with the number 100. Interestingly you'll discover that the sound of your voice will also help to carry you deeper into this wonderful quality of relaxation. After each number double your mental relaxation. After each number allow your mind to grow twice as peaceful, calm and relaxed. If you do this you'll discover that by the time you reach the number 95 or sooner, you've relaxed your mind so beautifully so perfectly that you've actually relaxed all the rest of the numbers right on out of your mind. There just won't be any more numbers there for a while and it will feel great. Start with the idea of wanting that to happen. You'll see how quickly and easily it will happen. Those numbers will go if you tell them to, and it will feel great.

All right("John"), I'd like you to slowly begin counting backwards, out loud, starting with the number 100 and relax those numbers right on out. (John "100") Now double your mental relaxation already, just let them fade and grow dim and distant.

[Client looses the numbers]

And they're gone, aren't they? (client/patient affirms) The mind is relaxed and the body is relaxed and the mind and the body continue much more with each gentle breath you exhale.

Emerging the Client

In a moment I'm going to count from one to five. With each number a healthy wave of positive energy will flow from the top of your head through your body to the tips of your toes. Each wave will grow stronger than the one before, refreshing, and healthy, and at the same time peaceful and calm. When I reach the number 5, I'll snap my fingers you'll open your eyes feeling wonderfully refreshed, healthy, revitalized, re-energized, and that wonderful feeling is just going to stay with you.

Sample Use of a Group Induction

A great way to build a thriving practice is by doing groups. Doing group sessions for adult education programs, fraternal organizations, and civic groups can bring income and get you free advertisement. Below you will find a sample of an induction that is usable with both groups and for individuals (with minor modifications).

Therapist to Group:

I want you to place your feet flat on the floor and just place your hands on your lap. Close your eyes for a moment and imagine a pleasant place or feeling. Now hold onto that image or feeling. [Pause for a few seconds] Now I want you to open your eyes and look at me. Focus only on me. Look right here until I ask you to close your eyes once again. In a few moments I'm going to begin counting backwards from ten to one, by the time I reach the number one you'll be in a deep wonderful state of relaxation. It will be like daydreaming, or relaxing at the beach, only much better. No matter how deeply you go into hypnosis your subconscious mind will always hear the sound of my voice and I can always bring you out of hypnosis simply by counting from one to five and asking you to emerge. Everything we do will be totally beneficial for you and it will feel great, so forget about me and enjoy the feeling.

You may hear other sounds, but it doesn't matter. If

anything extraneous sounds will help to carry you deeper into relaxation, and you can just allow that to happen. So just leave everything to me and enjoy. Take a mini mental vacation. Have a massage for the mind. Just enjoy!

Now I would like you to keep your eyes open until I ask you to close them. Take a deep breath in and fill up your lungs. Now exhale and just let your body sag, loose and limp. Now take a second deep breath in, imagine yourself breathing in relaxation, now exhale and just release any stress tension or irritation, let it go. Now take a third deep breath in, fill up your lungs, now exhale, and close your eyes, and sleep. Imagine that moment between awake and asleep when you drift off to sleep at night. Let sleep be on your mind, and as you float, drift and dream notice how good you feel. Peaceful, calm, relaxed. Feel that relaxation as it drifts through your body. Feel it drifting through your scalp. Down over your forehead, to your eyebrows, gently over you eyelids, as they grow warm and heavy. Let it drift down over your nose and mouth. Relax the muscles of your jaw. Now notice the muscles of your neck, as they grow so limp and relaxed that your head just hangs loose, limp and wonderfully relaxed. It feels wonderful and it just keeps getting better. Because it's normal and natural to relax when taking gentle breaths each gentle breath you take carries you deeper and because it's in your best interest in accomplishing your goal, you allow that to happen. Feel that relaxation as it drifts down from your neck and shoulders, down your arms, right down to the tips of your fingers. Let it flow down through your body to the tips of your toes as you relax even more deeply. It's such a wonderful feeling to relax, and the deeper you go the better you feel.

Right now you have no place to go, nothing to do, no problem to solve, simply relax and enjoy this wonderful quality of relaxation. Deeper with each gentle breath you take.

And on the count of 10, feel your body relaxing loose and limp. Just let that relaxation grow with each and every breath you exhale. It's as if you were relaxing at: [LOCATION PLEASANT FOR THE PERSON / e.g.: park, beach, etc.]. Imagine yourself [At LOCATION], white billowy clouds float across the pale blue sky as a gentle breeze blows over the surface of your skin. Feel the warmth of the sun on your face, feel the warmth of the sun on your body, and as that warm wonderful feeling soaks in, every muscle, joint and fiber relaxes much more. On the count of 9, It feels wonderful, and it just keeps getting better. It feels peaceful and calm, nothing can disturb you now. Deeper and sounder on the count of eight, as you drift and float and dream. And on the count of seven notice how pleasantly heavy your body feels, especially your arms, especially your head. Your head is so heavy now the muscles of your neck so loose, limp and relaxed, that even though you know you could move your head if you really wanted to it just isn't worth the effort. And your head rests loose and limp, and you allow that to happen.

And on the count of six, you're in my circle of relaxation nothing can disturb you now. Perfectly comfortable, peaceful calm and relaxed. Each gentle breath you take will carry you deeper. And because it's in your best interest in accomplishing your very important goal, you allow that to happen. Deeper and sounder, floating and drifting like in a dream, only better than a dream and it just keeps getting better.

And on the next count I'm going to help you to go very deeply into hypnosis by touching you on the shoulder. At the moment, at the instant that I touch you feel your body relaxing loose and limp and allow a wave of gentle relaxation to pass from my hand, passing gently through you, to carry you even deeper into this wonderful quality of relaxation. Just let yourself float, drift, dream into this beautiful feeling, enjoy this wonderful feeling. So go very deeply now into this deep wonderful hypnotic sleep, enjoy this wonderful feeling on the count of five (touch each person on the shoulder while repeating the above suggestion). [Note: if the group is too large simply omit this suggestion.]

And on the count of four, notice your arms growing even heavier. They feel like heavy weights hanging by your side. It feels wonderful and curiously interesting that your arms could be so loose and limp and wonderfully relaxed. They feel so heavy now they feel as if they're dragging, pulling, wanting to fall by your side, and if I help them to do that they just fall and hang by your side loose, limp, and lazy. Each gentle breath carries you deeper, you allow that to happen way, down deep floating, drifting, like in a beautiful dream. Way down deep. Deeper and sounder with each gentle breath you take

Deeper and sounder on the count of three you feel wonderful, refreshed, peaceful and calm. Each gentle breath continues to carry you deeper because it's in your best interest to accomplish your very important goal you allow that to happen. Deeper and sounder on the count of two you feel wonderful, refreshed and healthy. The deeper you go the better you feel and it just keeps getting better.

And on the next count I give you the ability to go so deeply into hypnosis that you drift easily and safely to that special and magical place where anything that you can imagine you can accomplish easily and effortlessly. So go very deeply now into this deep wonderful hypnotic sleep, very deeply on the count of one. Each gentle breath continues to carry you deeper. You feel wonderful, refreshed, peaceful and calm. Floating, drifting, like in a beautiful dream only better than a dream. Way down deep.

Chapter 6

OBJECTIVITY IN A PROFESSIONAL PRACTICE

THE DESIRE TO HELP OTHERS

The desire to help others is something to take pride in. The difference between a layperson with the desire to help others, and a therapist with that same desire, is the trained ability to direct that desire in the most productive way. It is the ability, through education, training, and experience, to put emotional "reactions" aside and to do the job you have been asked (and paid) to do.

One common mistake that I notice with many new and aspiring therapists is that their heart often overpowers their head. When this happens, the client/patient often does not get the benefit they had hoped for. Although empathy plays a role in therapy, it doesn't follow that training and common sense should go out the window. In his or her zeal to "save" the person, the inexperienced therapist puts heart and sole into efforts to help that person, often becoming more invested in the person's life than is the client/patient. Caring, and wanting to help, is not enough. Stepping in and attempting to save the person is neither productive, nor in the person's best interest. For success, the client/patient MUST be invested in the process to a greater extent than any other person. Often, the very reason the person has been unable to overcome a problem or accomplish goal(s), is because that person cannot be objective about his or her own life (Note: The person that we most lie to is our self). Those close to that person as well are often unable to be objective. It is the therapist's job to help them look at things from a different mountain or valley. If the therapist becomes emotionally involved, and loses his or her objectivity, it becomes a situation of the blind leading the blind.

The best resource that a therapist has to help a person achieve his or her goals is objectivity. If that were not true, anyone who simply "cared" and wanted to help would qualify as a therapist. We all know that this is not the case. To the contrary, well-intentioned friends and relatives are often counterproductive to positive change. Their sympathy and empathy often serve only to keep the person stagnant in the life problems that they profess a desire to overcome. Frequently these people are in fact enablers. Only through self-honesty can one move forward. Sympathy and consoling friends frequently sabotage the person's need to accept responsibility for, and power in their own lives.

Both empathy and sympathy can be virtuous, however, my personal opinion is that they are both highly overrated when it comes to providing competent therapy. A client/patient can get sympathy from their best friend, dog, or mother. Although a certain level of empathy by the therapist is acceptable, an overabundance will cloud the therapist's ability to see the broader picture of what is being presented by the person seeking help.

CLIENT/PATIENT FAMILIARITY

Regardless of our personal impressions of a person, it is important to remember that we only know that person by way of the brief window of time and experience that we have with them. No matter how the person impresses us, we don't really know them at all. Often during these brief hours the person will put there best foot forward (as most of us do when meeting someone for the first time). As well, the client/patient usually wants to solicit the therapist as an ally, and will expose to the therapist only those traits he or she wants you to see. The person is not always being honest with the therapist. In fact, they are not always honest with themselves. Simply because that person perceives his or her life situation to be so, it does not mean that their view has any basis in reality (other than within his or her own mind). Remember, in most cases, you know absolutely nothing about that person except for what they have told you. If you were to talk to others who know your client/patient, especially those not supportive of that person, you would likely get an entirely different picture of that person.

In a number of situations, I have worked with interns and students who say of almost every client, "Oh he (or she) is so nice". My reply is usually… "You don't know that! You just met him (or her). He or she may really suck!" The reality of life is that not everyone is nice. Some people are completely out of touch (that's often why they are having problems). Other people are just stinkers. Likewise, some people will be genuinely nice. It is important to remember that as a therapist you will encounter all kinds.

My point in saying this is simple, we should never qualify whether the client/patient is a nice person or a jerk. In fact, it is a non-issue. We are there to help. It is irrelevant if we like the person or not. A professional puts likes and dislikes aside and makes a sincere attempt to help the person accomplish his or her goal. After all, the greater the problem(s), the more the professional therapist is needed. By accepting the person as he or she is, and seeing him or her with clarity, we can more effectively move that person from point "A" to point "B".

DR. HOLDER'S RULES FOR THERAPY

Following are some suggestions that I give to my students. I have found that by following these simple rules the therapist can improve his or her success rate, increase his or her practice, and lead a less stressful professional life.

1. Hypnosis/hypnotherapy is a science, not mysticism.
2. Don't be more invested in the person's problem than they are.
3. See the whole person (good and bad).
4. Remember, you only know the person through the narrow window of time that you share with them.
5. It's the client/patient's life… you can't live it with or for them.
6. You can't save people from themselves.
7. For success, place the power in the hands of the client/patient.

Your success as a therapist depends on your ability to objectively apply the training and knowledge that you have gathered. If your vantage point is no different than that of your client/patient then you are no better equipped to help them move forward than they have been in the past without you. By offering a new prospective, by looking at things from a new mountain or valley, you can help them achieve their goals.

Chapter 7

The Professional Hypnotherapist

THERAPY: THERAPIST'S PREJUDICES, BIASES, AGENDAS, AND ETHICS

In any profession there are those who are in the profession for the right reasons and those that are in the profession for frivolous reasons. Although there may be many reasons that people become involved in therapeutic professions, the vast majority can be grouped into three areas. First, are those therapists who desire to help people by empowering the client or patient in his or her own life. These are the therapists with no preconceived agenda for the client other than helping the individual to overcome barriers for development and to maximize his or her potential as a unique individual.

Second, are those therapists who want to "save" people from their "lost ways". To save the client, from even themselves if necessary, and to direct them toward the kind of life the therapist envisions for that person. Of course for this approach to make sense, the therapist must assume that he or she has some divine insight whereby he or she knows more about what goals are appropriate for the client than anyone else on the planet (even though the therapist has probably known the person for only a brief time).

The third type of therapist (and I use the term therapist lightly in this circumstance) is the therapist who thinks that being a therapist (especially those in complementary/alternative methods like hypnosis/hypnotherapy) is just "cool". They get an ego boost from having people come to them with their problems. They are generally more interested in their own personal ego gratification than in giving to, or helping others. These people not only do the client a disservice but also are usually the first ones to belittle other therapists, spread gossip, and cause us as a profession to appear adolescent and less than professional. [Note: people who are truly confident and centered have no need for ego gratification provided through worship from clients, nor are they subject to the insecurities and fear that creates professional jealousy and the need to be destructive to colleagues.]

Obviously, we should aspire to be within the first set of criteria, avoid the second, and have disdain with the third. It is important to realize that true strength comes from within. It does not come as a result of the hero worship from others, or at the expense of others through manipulation, gossip or belittlement. Strength comes from confidence, love of life, and openness to knowledge.

PERSONAL PERCEPTIONS

Perhaps one of the most difficult things for any human being to do is to view the situations and circumstances of others objectively. We all tend to frame things relative to our own life experience. At the same time, an objective perspective is one of the most important qualities in being a competent therapist. In my opinion, any therapist who attempts to sway clients to his or her "belief system", or preach any doctrine of any type (within clinical setting) is not practicing therapy, he or she is preaching. If preaching is someone's calling then by all means they should go into that profession. It is a noble one. Preaching of a personal belief system or ideology should not, however, be included as part of clinical therapy.

When I mention preaching understand that I am not specifically speaking about the preaching of a religious doctrine. I am speaking to the issue of therapists with strong convictions to a particular philosophy, or to a particular agenda or bias who choose to indoctrinate clients or patients in that ideology. I am speaking about therapists who have either strong social, moral, political, or philosophical views that they feel compelled to "teach" to others. There is nothing wrong with having strong convictions so long as we do not let those personal convictions flow over into a client's therapy session. Those of us with strong convictions about how we could "make the world a better place" (and I include myself in this group), must be ever vigilant to keep our personal prejudices and agendas separate from our therapeutic work… no matter how convinced we may be that his or her view is the most valid and/or could "save" the client. A therapist is not there to promote his or her personal views. A therapist should be there for the express purpose of helping the client accomplish his or her goal(s).

SEPARATION

There are two important reasons to maintain a separation between the therapy, and the personal beliefs and the agendas of the therapist. First is what I call the rescuer complex. One of the pitfalls that I have seen many therapists fall into develops from the very fact that people often come to us at a point of weakness in their lives. They are asking, sometimes begging, for help and direction. It is easy, therefore, for the therapist to take on the cloak of rescuer. As well, especially with those newer in practice, the therapist may feel somewhat flattered that people expect and/or perceive him/her to have "all the answers" and the ability to solve their problem. This "ego-stroking" can further propel an inexperienced therapist into the role of "Knight in Shining

Armor" or "Mother Superior" (depending on gender). It is not our job to be rescuers. It is our job to empower the client and to give him/her the tools to take control of his or her own life. Our goal as therapists should be to "work ourselves OUT of a job" as quickly as possible. Just as a good parent raises a child to be independent and self sufficient, we should never seek to have our clients dependent on us. Ethically, morally, and professionally it is our job to bring the client to the point where they don't need us and to do that as quickly as possible.

The second reason for keeping personal biases out of therapy is simple. Our job is to do what the client has paid us to do. That's a pretty simple concept… A no-brainer, or so one would think. Unfortunately, some therapists fall into another mindset that I call the "Guru Complex" or "Wiseman (wise-woman) Complex". They somehow feel that due to their education, training, or maybe just because they're so darn brilliant and perceptive, that he or she (the therapist) knows better what the person should want and what he or she needs then anyone else… including the person themselves. No matter how wise a therapist thinks he or she is it is important to remember and to accept that our individual views are only personal opinion and our perception based on our individual life experience. Our perceptions, like everyone else's, are just opinion… nothing more. As a professional our only job is to do what the client paid us to do.

EDUCATED GUESS

We all know that physicians are not infallible, nor should we expect them to be. Even the most competent physician is only making educated guesses based on his or her training, experience and education, along with the quality of the data that he or she has acquired, from which to base a diagnosis (which is in fact an educated guess). For any therapist to consider that he or she some greater power is both presumptuous and egotistical. All therapeutic programs that we design and implement on our client's behalf are merely educated guesses based on our knowledge, training, and clinical experience. We (as clinicians) are not clergy or wise men (wise-women) and should not take on that robe. Our job is to help the client accomplish their goal. When we do this, we enhance both the public and professional image of hypnosis and hypnotherapy. We bring honor to the profession. We show ourselves to be true professionals.

Let me take this concept out of the therapeutic context with the following analogy. Imagine this… What if you hired a carpenter to build a deck off of the back of your house and later you came home to find that the carpenter had remodeled your kitchen instead because he felt that you needed a new kitchen more so than the deck that you had contracted him to build. You would probably be very displeased. Clients/patients come to us with a goal. We have one job, and one job only. That is to help the person achieve his or her goal as directly as possible. Your worth as a therapist will be defined by the following... The people that come to you for help must feel empowered, happy, and accomplished in what they set out to achieve, when they are finished their therapy with you.

WISDOM

I commend any person who has deep spiritual beliefs, moral views, and honorable convictions. I applaud those with a healthy philosophy of life that they want to share with others. The therapy session, however, should not be used as a pulpit for our personal agendas and beliefs. We need simply to be caring, honest, ethical, and competent. That is the best that we can give our clients. So if you ever catch yourself bringing your own personal agendas into session with a client

I suggest that you ask yourself this simple question. Do you really think that you have the infinite wisdom to judge and decide how everyone else should think, believe, and feel? If the answer is "no", then it is obvious what you must do. You must keep your personal biases, prejudices, and agendas out of the therapy session. If by chance someone answers that question with a "yes", he or she would be doing everyone concerned a great favor if they considered another career. We (therapists) are there to serve and to guide those who come to us to the accomplishment of "THEIR" goal(s), not our goal for them. The ability to do this is what separates the competent professional from the novice.

ESTABLISHING DIRECTION

We as hypnotherapists are "navigators of the mind". It is our job to guide a client or patient toward the accomplishment of a pre-determined goal. The process is simple. A client solicits the help of a hypnotherapist for the purpose of accomplishing a specific goal. The hypnotherapists after conducting an intake, will structure a therapy that is appropriate and practical with the aim of accomplishing that goal. During the intake, the hypnotherapist must formulate a plan. How will he or she move that client toward the client's goal in the simplest and most efficient manner? Developing this plan is crucial to successful therapy. If we (the hypnotherapist) are the navigators, then it stands to reason that we must map out a way to get from point "A" to point "B" before starting the journey. If we do not have a plan, then the client may as well stay home and meditate, contemplate, or purchase a generic self-help tape or book. The results would be similar and they would save the hypnotherapist's fee.

HYPNOSIS AND MEDITATION

I am frequently asked, "what is the difference between hypnosis and meditation?" The difference is simple. Meditation is free form and hypnotherapy is therapist driven. This difference is what makes we hypnotherapists, "navigators of the mind". Let me explain the similarities and differences between meditation and hypnotherapy in practical terms.

In both meditation and hypnotherapy, we are attempting to achieve the somnambulistic state (Note: The somnambulistic state provides an environment for acceptance of suggestion that will be durable). It is here that the similarity ends and the two part ways. In meditation, it is impossible for the person meditating to create and implement suggestion. This is so because… in order to formulate suggestion, it would be necessary for the person to bring the conscious mind into play. Bringing the conscious mind into play will deteriorate the depth of trance effectively bringing the person out of somnambulism.

True meditation is "free form". Once the meditative state is achieved (this will usually be somnambulism or deeper for those who have mastered meditation), the subconscious mind finds a level of comfort and then explores at that level. Effectively, the person will tap into the creative and beneficial properties of their subconscious. It is, however, a non-directed journey. (Note: Some would say that "guided meditation" is the exception to this rule. I suggest to you that what people refer to as guided meditation is not meditation at all. It is, in fact, hypnosis. Observe the methodology and content of guided meditation and I am sure that you will agree).

With hypnosis and hypnotherapy, the somnambulistic state will be achieved but that is where the similarity ends. The remainder of the process is totally different. Hypnosis is simply a tool used to entice the conscious mind to step aside so that we can speak directly to the subconscious mind. The heightened state of suggestibility that results from this is our venue for facilitating positive change. This difference between meditation and hypnotherapy begins early on within the pre-talk and consultation. This is where you (the hypnotherapist) gather the necessary information that will enable you to navigate your client, as per his or her wishes, to the accomplishment of his or her goal(s). In contrast to meditation, the person tells you what he or she would like to accomplish. After inducing hypnosis and achieving the appropriate depth of trance (for most therapy, somnambulism) the hypnotherapist, based on the information gathered during the intake, will guide the person to the accomplishment of the previously stated goal. The person has no need to self-direct the session (which would in fact deteriorate trance). That is precisely why he or she has come to you. They place their trust in you to guide or navigate them to the accomplishment of their goal. They depend on you to facilitate positive change within them.

ESTABLISHING THE PATH

A hypnotherapist must be able to direct and navigate the client or patient as per that person's intent for the session. The pre-talk sets this plan in motion. This is where the hypnotherapist must establish rapport, gain compliance and set the perimeters for the work he or she will be doing. If you do not set appropriate perimeters early on, you may lose the ability to navigate the person to the requested destination. Furthermore, if the perimeters are not set, therapeutically, you may lose the effectiveness of the session altogether.

Your clients or patients come to you because they have faith in your ability to navigate them past the reefs and shoals that have in the past have held them back, to the accomplishment of their goal. It is your job therefore to take the reigns and gracefully guide them to that end.

PRE-TALK AND WAKING SUGGESTIONS

In the pre-talk, I always emphasize that I want the person to relax and leave all the work to me. I tell them that they have the great and wonderful opportunity to take a trip without leaving the farm. Facilitating this attitude within the person is important. It gives them permission to relax, get comfortable, and enjoy the session. It takes the pressure off. This will help immensely is getting the conscious mind to step aside. One way that I get this message across is outlined in the short script that follows. This or something like it is always a part of my pre-talk.

Dr. H.:
John (or whoever) you know what's really neat about hypnosis?

Subject:
(Will usually stare at you blankly for a moment).

Dr. H.:
In most things that we do in life, the harder we try, the better we do... Right!

Subject:
Yes.
[Note: I'm always going for the yes answer and compliant responses.]

Dr. H.:
The great thing about hypnosis is, that the less you try, and the more you simply forget about it relax, and enjoy it, the

better you do. Isn't that great!

Subject:
Yes.

[The person has now accepted permission to relax and just "let it happen".]

It is important as well that the person follow the therapist's instructions completely. I find that therapists who lack experience often let the session get away from them. They lose sight of the goal the client originally indicated he or she would like to accomplish. They inadvertently let the client lead them off track (effectively converting the session into a dysfunctional guided meditation). This frequently is a result of the therapist becoming intrigued by, or confused by, something that happens within the session. He or she then allows curiosity, or panic, to lead them off track. It may also simply be that the hypnotherapist had no map in place before the session began. This results in a situation of "the blind leading the blind." It is impossible to lead if you have no idea where you are going. In any event, it is the therapist's job to pace and lead. It is not appropriate or effective to pace and follow.

CASE STUDY

Allow me to share an experience of mine with you that will illustrate the importance of planning and navigating the client or patient. While working with a gentleman, in only moments, he went into the Esdaile state. Statistically, it is said, that about 1 in 1000 hypnosis subjects will do this (I actually find it to be more like 1 in every 400 to 500). In any event, my client was enjoying the experience so much that when I asked him to emerge he would not. I instructed him again to emerge from hypnosis (using a different and firmer approach) and he did so. On our next meeting, I immediately set out to firm up my client's willingness to comply under all appropriate circumstances (Personally, in therapy sessions, I like to know that my client and I are always on the same page). This facilitates a more productive session. I began the session with a short pre-talk to assure that I would remain in the navigator's seat during all subsequent sessions, regardless of depth of trance. The pre-talk went something like this.

Dr. H:

Bob (not his real name), on our last session you went very deeply into hypnosis. That was great wasn't it.

Bob:

It sure was. (He went on to explain that he felt he experienced something spiritual and very special. He further stated that he really didn't want to come back when I asked him to).

Dr. H.:

I know that is so. When I asked you the first time to emerge, you wanted to stay longer. I had to ask you twice to emerge. I'm glad that you enjoyed the experience. I know it is a wonderful feeling. It is important however that you follow my instructions completely at all times. Timing is of the essence in achieving your goal. When I ask you to come back, I need you to bring what you have acquired back with you at that exact moment. Only by doing this will you fully achieve your goal. It's all in the timing. For that reason, I am going to do the following. Today, I am going to place what I call a "dormant seal" within your subconscious mind. This is how it will work. That seal will remain dormant and inactive unless while in hypnosis I say the words, "I seal you out". If I must ever say those words to you while you are in hypnosis, you will emerge from hypnosis. As well, you will be sealed out of that depth of hypnosis completely and for all time unless I remove the seal. I know that you enjoy that wonderful feeling and want to go back to it again and again. I want to take you there again too. But if we go there, you must follow my instructions at all times, including when I ask you to return. Do you understand me?

Bob:

Yes

I then proceeded with the session. After inducing hypnosis (but before deepening) I repeated the information regarding the dormant seal as a post-hypnotic suggestion. From that moment on, even in the deepest levels of hypnosis, I maintained the ability to navigate "Bob" at all times. Only by maintaining the ability to navigate the client can an effective therapy session take place. For your general information it has never been my intent to use the dormant seal even though I could do so. The suggestion that they will not be able to return to that feeling has always been enough to inspire compliance.

THE CHILD IN US

Along with gathering the necessary information to conduct a session, it is important to recognize that when speaking to someone in a hypnotic state, we are speaking to the childlike qualities within that person. The subconscious mind will lock on to all suggestions that are positive and acceptable. It is important to structure the session in a way that will entice that child-like part of us to follow. The stereotypical monotone hypnotist is far from the ideal model. Much better results are achieved by making each session fun and interesting. Your client will be much more likely to follow your lead when you use phrases like… "Wouldn't that be great" or "You'd like that wouldn't you" or "This will be fun. You'll really enjoy this." Imagine what phrases would have inspired you to cooperate as a child, then use them with your clients. You will find this more effective than a clinical or mystical approach (monotone etc.). As well, you will gain greater satisfaction from the work you do.

CONCLUSION

Those who seek you out expect that you will help them. They put their goals and aspirations in your hands. This makes your job easy if you pick up the ball from there. You must direct and navigate the session relative to the person's pre-determined and stated goal. If you remain in the navigator's seat, your success rate will increase and your practice will grow. All it takes is a little planning and an alert and perceptive mind.

Chapter 8

Formatting Great Sessions

PRIORITIZING

For your hypnotherapy client or patient to receive maximum benefit from your suggestions, it is essential that suggestions be given in the best possible order. During the intake, a therapist should gather information that will allow him or her to construct a therapeutic plan and to formulate suggestions that will be meaningful to the subject. As well, and of equal importance, the therapist must decide in what order the suggestions should be made. This order will have a direct bearing on the effectiveness of the session. The order of suggestions should be based on the subject's hierarchy of importance to the motivators that the therapist has recorded during the intake. This is a very important aspect in structuring a session. The reason is simple… to a large degree the effectiveness of your suggestions will be a product of the compounding and prioritization of the suggestions.

COMPOUNDING

In brief, compounding is a process used to strengthen suggestion through repetition, and follow-up of that suggestion with complementary suggestion and with repetition. The first suggestion that you make is, at first, weak. The second suggestion strengthens the first and therefore the second becomes the weakest and the first becomes stronger. This progression will continue throughout the session. Also, and particularly so with direct suggestion, it is important to repeat each suggestion numerous times. I recommend to my students that direct suggestions be repeated seven or eight times. After seven or eight repetitions you will reach a point of diminishing return. Making a suggestion only once or twice will probably not provide the compounding effect that you are seeking.

HOW TO FORMAT YOUR SESSION

During the intake, I suggest that you jot down the person's significant motivators. Any statement reflecting why the person is motivated to make the changes they desire should be rephrased into positive and acceptable suggestions. The person usually does not provide this information in sequence of priority or in progression of relative value. As you receive the information, it is up to you to determine which motivators are most significant to the person. This decision will be based on the overall content derived out of the intake process. I use a very simple process to create the order of suggestion. I simply refer to the information that I have jotted down during the intake and then I number the motivators (and corresponding suggestions) by priority. If you do this you will find it easy to structure the session in a meaningful order. You simply go by the numbers that you have assigned each motivator and corresponding suggestion. Make the most significant item of the list "number one" and work your way down.

This is a quick, easy, and effective way to structure a powerful session. The notations need only be brief, so there is little to write as you are moving through the intake. As well, you have simultaneously created a written record of your session. This is great for your record keeping. It also helps you in organizing subsequent sessions with that person. You have a record of where you have been and what you have done. This might not be of concern to someone who is working with only a minimal number of people, but if you plan on working with more than a handful of people each year you will need a system. People early in their career often think that they can trust it all to memory. That is a mistake. Keeping accurate records will become terribly important when you are working with dozens of people each week, so if you are not already doing it… get in the habit of keeping good records/charts. It is impossible to keep everyone's therapy straight by memory alone. It is important from both a therapeutic standpoint and from a professional liability standpoint to keep accurate records. A professional always keeps accurate records.

At the beginning of a follow-up session I conduct what you might call a mini-intake. I find out what suggestions from the previous session had the strongest effect in helping the client/patient achieve his or her goals. It is a simple matter to adjust the follow-up session to fit current needs. You simply re-number, add, or delete, any suggestion in order to proceed in the most positive and productive way. By prioritizing suggestions you will increase your success rate. At the same time you make your job easier and more enjoyable. It will save you time as well and that's important if you have, or hope to have, a busy practice.

VISUALIZATION: LET THE CLIENT OR PATIENT PAINT THE PICTURE

Visualization can be a powerful tool. Over the years I have noticed that with many students, interns, and also with practicing hypnotherapists, often the best results using visualization are not achieved because of a tendency to overdo the detail when developing the visualization(s). One might say in response… What harm could there be in developing detailed visualizations with a person? The answer is simple. We all perceive the world around us differently.

Even with something as simple as a flower, each person finds different characteristics of that flower appealing (or not so appealing). Some find beauty in the appearance, others in the fragrance. Still others may associate that same flower with itchy eyes and sneezing (allergies). Each individual will have a unique perception that will undoubtedly be different from that of another person. The bottom line is that your perception of a visualization created by you for someone else might be perceived in a significantly different way than you expected by the other person.

My advice is simple… "Give the person the brush and let them paint the picture on their own." This being said, it actually creates a more meaningful visualization when your input is minimal. Provide a general framework to facilitate the visualization and then let the person fill in the detail.

Another important thing to remember is that some people can more easily visualize detail than others. If your suggestions are too detailed for the person he or she may be incapable of creating what you have suggested. This will become frustrating to the person. The conscious mind will be drawn back, questioning whether or not "it is working," or "if they (or you) are doing it right." This will deteriorate the depth of trance and adversely affect the quality of the session. Every person processes information differently and at different speeds. No therapist possesses an "exact" indicator as to what the person is visualizing at any given moment. If you are too detailed, and the person is either lagging behind, or a step ahead of you, it will become frustrating to them. By providing only the simplest framework within the visualization there is more latitude for both you and the subject to move easily through the visualization in synchronization.

KEEP IT SIMPLE

Simplicity is always best. As an example… If I suggest that it's a hot summer day and that the person is enjoying a cool grape Popsicle, I have already assumed that the person enjoys the heat of the sun and that he or she likes grape Popsicles. If he or she hates grape Popsicles, or is sensitive to sunlight, I may have already shot myself in the foot. It would be more productive (and less problematic) to suggest a comfortable day and a refreshing gentle breeze. The details about what is comfortable are better left to the subject. So to, is the meaning of what is refreshing and gentle. I might suggest that the person is enjoying a safe and beautiful place that was created just for them. I allow them to fill in the details (give them the brush and let them paint the picture). By using this simple approach, I am able to pace and lead more easily because I have built in a margin of error between the speed at which the person processes information and the speed at which I am providing the information.

COMPATIBILITY

Suggestions and visualizations must fit the person's nature. They must be comfortable and acceptable to them. For example: no offense intended to any of you who happen to like camping but I for one don't like to camp. My idea of roughing it is "no room service." In my opinion, mankind worked for centuries to have the luxury of cooking, bathing, and going to the bathroom inside and I'm going to enjoy those benefits. As well, I see no reason to swat mosquitoes and bare intense heat after someone went to all of the trouble to invent air-conditioning. You can bet then, that if someone suggested to me that I was comfortably snuggled in my sleeping bag in a cozy tent it would NOT represent my idea of a good time. By the same token, I am sure that if I were to simply ask you to imagine a place that is safe, comforting, and pleasant, you could create an image that is significant and meaningful to you. Your image would better represent that idea than anything I could dream up on your behalf. If I were to instruct you on the details of such a place, (imposing my image upon you), you can easily see why it would be less effective. The more complex the suggestions the greater the opportunity for the person to visualize something that is as equally unpleasant for him or her, as it may be pleasant for you. The simpler the suggestions the less the opportunity to create images that are incompatible with the person's likes and dislikes.

GIVE THEM THE BRUSH

You can lead them to water but off course they must drink on their own. The best and most productive images are those that come from within the person's own mind. Nothing that you can create will be as meaningful for the person as the pictures they themselves paint. If a person has great visualization skills, you can utilize that to facilitate a terrific session. Conversely, too much of a good thing can be worse than nothing at all. Planting the seed and allowing the rest to grow naturally will develop the best possible visualizations and promote a productive session. If you simply give the person the brush, he or she will create a place that is meaningful to them. Both you and your client or patient will have a more productive and pleasant session. In facilitating visualizations, less is more.

THE POWER OF FAITH AND SUGGESTION

The core principle of hypnotherapy is to create a heightened state of suggestibility in order to introduce positive suggestion. These suggestions will then facilitate positive changes in attitude, behavior and perspective. The ability to help a person succeed in accomplishing their goal(s) depends significantly on your client's faith and trust that these changes are not only possible, but also likely. On a second visit, the conversation went something like this.

Dr. H.:
You've been doing well this past week I trust.

George: (not his real name):

I've been doing great. My stress levels are down and I find that I'm able to cope calmly with the pressures that were setting me off before. I'm not sure though if it's the hypnosis. It could just be the power of suggestion because I expected something to happen by coming to you.

I assured him that it was the power of suggestion. I explained (again) that hypnosis is exactly that. He had simply never thought of hypnosis in that light. Our vehicle for facilitating change is the power of suggestion. The cornerstone of accomplishment is a positive attitude… The faith that "it" will in fact happen. This coupled with a true desire to achieve a goal is a powerful combination. The power of suggestion is closely intertwined with faith and expectation. Without that faith and expectation, suggestion may not overcome negative perception.

THE CHILD

We are in essence speaking to the child within when we speak to a person who is in hypnosis. The child doesn't analyze or rationalize. It will either like and accept a suggestion, or it will not.

Personally, when someone comes to me for help, I am not concerned with the attitude he or she had yesterday or last week. I am not concerned for that matter with what his or her attitude was when walking into my reception room. I'm only concerned with their perception and attitude at the time of induction. This is what is most often missed in preparation and in the pre-talk.

Below are four things to consider that will help you in creating faith and a positive "can do" attitude with those with whom you work.

1. Never Become Sidetracked or Drawn in by Negativity.

Many times people come to hypnotherapists with low self-esteem and a defeatist attitude. Often they come to us after exhausting all other options. They have failed... until now. They are beaten and feel incompetent. It is easy to inadvertently get caught up in this negativity without even noticing it. If you do this, it will shake his or her faith in himself and deteriorate your prospects for success. If you want a great success record, this is not where you want to go. Never allow yourself to be drawn into conversation centering on his or her past failures. Comments like, " Well, don't feel bad, none of us has success all of the time" will not inspire a person or give them faith in themselves. Instead, find out where they have succeeded. It doesn't matter in what or to what degree. What is important is that they begin to feel "As if they can."

For example, I was seeing someone who was very successful in business but felt like a personal failure because he couldn't stop smoking. He came to me with a very negative attitude. As he put it, "I'll give this hypnosis stuff a shot, but nothing else has worked so this probably won't either." How would you have addressed his comment? If you answered that you would tell him what a powerful tool hypnosis is, or something like that... BZZZZZT, next contestant please! Hypnosis isn't the issue here. The issue here is the person's attitude.

The first question I asked him was "What accomplishment of yours are you the most proud of?" His reply mostly revolved around his ability to start up and develop a lucrative business. I said to him, "That must have been tough. You probably had to overcome tremendous obstacles on the road to success. That's something to be very proud of." He agreed that he had done well in overcoming adversity and began to tell me about one of his experiences. This was just the window of opportunity that I was looking for. It was the perfect chance to change the negative attitude that he had walked through the door with. It was an opportunity to positively influence his perspective before induction.

I explained to him that the same powerful mind that accomplished so much could easily defeat a silly little cigarette. I told him that the problem to date had not been him. It was simply that he had been depending on external resources like patches and nicotine gum rather that his most valuable asset… his mind. I assured him that for anyone who had accomplished the wonderful things that he had accomplished, leading a healthy, smoke free life would be a cakewalk. He agreed. He was psyched. He was ready to go, and so was I. He now had the power and the faith in himself that he could accomplish his goal. Guess what! He doesn't smoke anymore. Always focus on the positive. Negative thoughts bring negative results. Positive thoughts bring positive results. One's perception usually becomes their reality. They believe (have faith in) it to be so, and thus it becomes a self-fulfilling prophecy. It's almost as if people want so badly to be correct that they will live out their belief, be it productive or detrimental to their lives. This is why it is so critically important to navigate the person toward a positive attitude.

2. Give Them a Positive Attitude and the Faith That He Or She Can Do It.

We can always find fault if we look for it. Likewise, we can always find a positive side to something if we look for it (e.g.: That man has only one leg, but he gets twice the life out of a pair of socks). It is not a client or patient's duty to come to you with a great attitude. It is up to the therapist to direct the person to a more productive attitude. This is accomplished by awakening them to the knowledge that he or she has always had the power for positive change within them. By convincing them (if only moments before inducing hypnosis) that he or she has the ability to accomplish what they've set out to do, they will accomplish their goal. In effect, they succeed due to your help in giving them the faith to know they can.

3. Create a YES Response Mechanism

Begin creating a "Yes" response from the moment you greet a person. From the moment someone walks through the door, I begin drawing "yes responses" from them. Virtually every question I ask and any statement that requires a response is designed to solicit a yes response. In effect, I am having them practice a "YES ATTITUDE." For example, I avoid statements like... "If you try, you can accomplish your goal today." A more positive approach would be to say to the person, "Today, I will help you accomplish your goal. Isn't that great (I nod my head "yes", and the person agrees with either a nod of the head or a "yes" response)". Then I might say, "You have the power, and I know that you are highly motivated. After all, that is why you are here, right!" (Again, I am nodding yes and getting the yes response back from the person). Never make comments like, "Do you think you can do it?" or "Will you try?" To your unpleasant surprise, you might get a negative response. Furthermore, avoid using the word try. Try is the disciple of defeat. It gives the person a back door out (e.g.: I didn't say I would do it, I just said that I would try).

4. Create a Positive Self-Image within the person

Explain that everyone experiences hypnosis a little differently and because of that, no one can do it wrong. Encourage the person along the way. Tell them how good they are doing. Focus on the positive things that they say and congratulate them on their "positive remarks". Even when I have someone, who's self esteem is in the dumpster, I always find something within that person that he or she takes pride in.

I recall one woman who came to me who was convinced that she was completely worthless and couldn't do anything right. After a few moments of listening to her self-condemnation I said… "Tell me what you enjoy doing most." She thought for a moment and then replied. "I like cooking". I said, "I know you must be a good cook. We generally do best the things we enjoy, don't we?" (as I nodded my head up and down.) She said, "Yes, I am a pretty good cook". "See" I said, "You do have wonderful qualities. I couldn't cook like that. I sometimes forget the recipe for ice." She laughed and was visibly more excited about her prospects for success. I helped her to see a quality that she possessed. Our conversation had helped her to gain faith in herself.

A POSITIVE BELIEF SYSTEM

This methodology is not so different from that of faith healers. If the belief structure is there, and the person expects it to happen (their goal), it usually will. To keep the belief system intact, it is also important to provide the client or patient with positive reinforcement and reasonable expectations. For example, if an obese woman came for weight loss and you were to imply that in six weeks they would look like a fashion model, when it didn't happen, the faith would be damaged. Reinforce positive and realistic goals. Encourage the person that the key to success is to consistently keep moving in a positive direction. That as long as they are pursuing a better quality of life, they are to be commended.

As a basic example, let's say a two-pack-a-day smoker came to you to stop smoking. After the first week, that person has not stopped completely but he or she has cut down to two cigarettes a day. Reprimanding the person for cheating with those two cigarettes would only diminish his or her chances for complete success. It would damage his or her faith in their ability to succeed. It would be more productive to congratulate the person on his or her "success". Encourage them by saying, "You are on the right path. You are well on your way to the full accomplishment of your goal. See how powerful your mind is. In only a few days, you've taken back almost all control of your life from tobacco. You're almost there. The rest will be a cakewalk for you. I'm so proud of you." These are empowering statements that give the person faith in themselves and the ability to succeed.

PRACTICE MAKES PERFECT

Whatever we practice to be, we become. Some people wait for a magical bolt of inspirational lightening to hit them or the spirit to move them. Personally, I believe that the behavior precedes the feeling. By having them practice self-talk and attitudes that are exemplary of having faith in one's self, a person begins to generate faith in themselves. The more one practices a positive attitude, the more positive their direction becomes. Will this method guarantee you success with every person? Of course it cannot. I know of no therapeutic or medical modality that can unconditionally guarantee success every time. What is important is that it will increase your success rate. It will move you toward your goal of helping more who come to you.

PURPOSE AND INTENT

Two of the most important components of a quality therapy session are purpose and intent. You must have both a goal and a plan to achieve that goal. Without purpose and intent a session will lack direction. A hypnotherapist's purpose and intent should be to empower the client or patient to the degree where he or she can accomplish their goal(s). A professional therapist should never take on the cloak of evangelist or Guru. We are not spiritual leaders. Therapists who fancy themselves in that role destroy the credibility of the profession and give ammunition to those who would like to see alternative wellness methods banished (or at the least absorbed by other more mainstream modalities). Our professional services are for the express purpose of assisting those that come to us in achieving their goal(s). If a person comes to a hypnotherapist to stop smoking, the therapist should help them to stop smoking. If they come to manage stress, the hypnotherapist should give them the tools to manage stress… nothing more, nothing less.

This may seem like a no-brainer. The truth is, however, that may times each year I encounter "therapists" that think it appropriate to direct the therapy session(s) to what they feel the person "really needs" rather than simply giving the person what he or she came for. Therapy promoting the therapist's agenda is not therapy at all. It is manipulation. It is not in the best interest of the client or patient nor is it in the best interest of the profession of hypnotherapy in general. Remember, if you hired a carpenter to build you a deck, you would not be happy to find that he had remodeled your kitchen instead because he thought that was a better idea. Providing a therapeutic service is no different. The power must always be in the hands of the client or patient.

PREPARATION

As in any undertaking, planning and preparation are essential. The intake is the time when this plan is formulated. I call this stage the "assessment" stage. This is parallel to or the equivalent of a physician forming a diagnosis. It is a time to collect information that will be utilized within the person's therapy and in the accomplishment of his or her stated goal. It is a time to both gain greater insight into the person's perception of themselves (and related events) as well as a time to create rapport by helping the person become more comfortable with you (the therapist).

The next stage is what I call "designed resolution." This would be the equivalent of a physician's treatment plan. [Note: These two stages, at times, may occur simultaneously or overlap]. The information collected during the assessment must be molded into a designed resolution. This strategic plan will move the person from where they are to where they want to be (the accomplishment of his or her goal). Consistently successful therapy does not happen by accident or through intuition or "feeling." It happens through careful planning. In the same way as Edison said that "success is ninety percent perspiration and ten percent inspiration," I suggest that quality therapy is ninety percent preparation and ten percent instinct.

In talking to practicing therapists, I am frequently shocked at the number of hypnotherapists who proceed with no plan at all. They keep no charts or records on those who come to them and structure no real "therapy." If hypnotherapy and other alternative wellness modalities ever wish to gain mainstream acceptance, then those in the profession must conduct themselves in a professional manner. Part of that professionalism is to be organized and to keep accurate records. A “professional” therapist will always develop a plan as to how he or she will resolve the person’s issue and then lead him or her to the accomplishment of that specified goal in the most expeditious fashion. To effectively do this the therapist must assess the problem, develop a plan of resolution, and then follow the plan to its conclusion.

Keeping copious notes in a “client/patient profile” (or chart) is essential to doing quality therapeutic work. After seeing many people all week, it would be virtually impossible for me to pick up where I left off at the last session without these valuable notes. Your notes should outline the assessment formed during the intake as well as the initial designed resolution (treatment plan). It should further indicate the suggestions that you included in the first and any subsequent sessions. This will enable you to do more of what has worked with a person and to discard what has not proven effective.

STRUCTURING SUGGESTIONS

The simplest and most effective way to structure and prioritize suggestion used in session is to take the information that the client/patient provides paraphrasing that information into positive suggestions. Then, number the suggestions in order of importance for the greatest value when compounding. The primary suggestion receives the number 1, the next most important the number 2, and so on. Later I can refer back to the numbering to know what suggestions were given and in what order.

These notes allow me to accurately follow up at subsequent sessions, and to maximize my efforts. This is especially important when the therapy is ongoing over a period of weeks or when someone returns after a period of time for the same or for a different issue. These notes will tell you what was discussed, what the goal of the session(s) was, what induction you used, what suggestions were made, and so on. As well, it is important to keep these records from a legal standpoint. You should always have documentation about what you did, and did not do with each person. Having a plan and keeping complete therapeutic records is a sign of a professional.

PARALLEL VS. DIRECTED

The information that you gather during the intake should be used in a "directed" fashion. It is important to have "unification of intent" when conducting a therapeutic session. The directed approach is when all information gathered during the intake is selectively structured into the session with all data pointing directly to the accomplishment of a specific goal. . This use of information results in a powerful session.

The parallel use of intake information creates a shotgun effect. Each item of data collected is used as a separate entity and/or randomly, with little or no direct application to one specific goal. This use of information results in a weak session. It is essential to have this "unification of intent" if you want to get the maximum effect from each session. All information must be used in harmony in a way that will move the person closer to the specified goal.

SIMPLICITY IS OFTEN THE KEY

I like the "KISS" (keep it simple stupid) philosophy. "LESS IS MORE"... "The shortest distance between two points is a straight line", and so on. Complicating therapy does not make it better. In fact, complication causes therapy to become more cumbersome for both the therapist and the client or patient. If you keep your sights on the specified goal, have a plan, and follow your plan, you will have success. Direct all information gathered (via your suggestions) toward that one specific goal and you will discover how easy it can be to conduct powerful sessions.

QUALITY THERAPY NON-LEADING STATEMENTS

In the past 35 years or so I have seen alternative wellness modalities come from relative obscurity to the brink of being accepted as mainstream. During this time I have also observed the field or hypnotherapy rise from being stereotyped with images of Count Dracula, to being viewed as a respected profession. One of my goals is to inspire those practicing hypnotherapy (and other alternative wellness methods) to present and conduct themselves in a professional way. That is the only way through which hypnotherapy (or any alternative method of wellness) will attain the full respect that it deserves. Not only is it in every practitioner's best interest to represent our profession(s) in a respectable way, it is imperative for the future of holistic and alternative health that we do so.

OUR JOB

As a hypnotherapist (or counselor) it is a person's job to assist others in achieving their goals. That is the only job. A true professional will never impose his or her own agenda into therapy sessions. As a professional it is critically important to leave personal agendas outside of the office walls. A therapist should never assume the roll of pastor, priest, or rabbi. If a person chooses to go to his or her spiritual leader for counseling that is a horse of a different color. He or she has gone to that spiritual leader for the express purpose of receiving counseling based upon that particular spiritual belief system. That is not the case when an individual chooses a professional clinical therapist or counselor. This holds true even if the therapist happens to be a man (or woman) of the cloth. In a clinical setting, those biases must be left outside.

We all have prejudices and biases. Anyone who says that they do not is either lying to you, or to themselves. One difference between a true professional and a want-to-be therapist, is the ability to keep those biases out of the therapy sessions. Clearly, those who bring their personal agendas into therapy sessions are, in my opinion, either self-righteous people who think that they have all of the answers, or they are simply inept therapists. Either way the client or patient looses.

NON-LEADING QUESTIONS

One way to assure a quality session is to formulate suggestions that are free from any personal (therapist's) agenda and to ask non-leading questions. Conversely, making suggestions formed with a therapist's agenda, or asking leading questions automatically perverts the session. In much the same way that politicians manipulate surveys and polls some therapists manipulate sessions. This is done sometimes by accident and sometime with intent (possibly even with good intent). Either way, the damage is the same. Below, as an example, you will find two imaginary political statements. They both represent the same situation but are framed to solicit two very different responses.

* Candidate John Smith wants to starve children by cutting

funding to poor countries.

* Candidate John Smith will vote against a tax increase sponsored by his opponent for the purpose of sending additional funds to an unstable third world government that is not using the funds effectively.

According to the first statement, most people would think that John Smith was a dirty rat. Reading the second statement, he would probably be perceived to be a responsible taxpayer's advocate.

Often poorly trained or unprofessional therapists do virtually the same thing within their sessions. Some therapists, based only on the initial contact, will decide what the person "really needs"... even if that differs from the person's stated goal. The therapist then proceeds based on the pre-determined result he or she "expects to get", rather than what the person came to the therapist to accomplish. This is certainly not in the person's best interest. For example, it has been discovered, (more frequently than anyone should be comfortable with), that many parents have been wrongly accused of child abuse due to the leading nature of questions within sessions conducted by overzealous therapists with a personal agenda. I am not saying that cases of child abuse don't exist. They certainly do. When they do exist the punishment should be severe. The sad part is that there have been too many caring parents wrongly convicted based on the testimony of psychologists or other therapists that started with an agenda of proving guilt rather than honestly seeking the truth. Those of you trained in hypnotherapy know the power of words. This is especially true when dealing with children. If an authority figure asks a child, "where did mommy or daddy touch you" that person, by virtue of that statement, may have just planted the idea that there has been inappropriate touching. That therapist probably entered into the interview with the preconceived idea that it did happen. That can be enough to taint the process. A more appropriate way to conduct the interview would be to ask the child general questions about every day life thereby letting the child develop the information. If the child volunteers that mommy or daddy touched him or her, the therapist might then say, oh really, describe that to me. This type of questioning may take longer, but it will result in a far more accurate and unbiased interview.

Non-leading questions and statements should be the norm, beginning with the pre-talk. The intake should be an information-gathering tool, not an indoctrination. Anything other than professional conduct jeopardizes the future for all alternative wellness professionals. You know the old saying: "Do something right and no one remembers. Do something wrong and no one forgets." This is so true, and one bad apple can spoil the whole bunch. Hypnotherapists (as well as all other therapists) must be self-policing and maintain the highest level of professionalism. This is the era where alternative wellness professions have the opportunity to demonstrate that they are valuable professionals. As in any emerging profession we must go over and above the call of duty to prove our value. Those who do anything else give ammunition to those who would like to see alternative modalities fail. This is our duty and obligation. It is our responsibility to ourselves and to our colleagues to uphold the highest levels of professionalism.

NOTHINGNESS

In Taoist philosophy (Lao Tsu / Tao Te Ching) it is said that "A truly good man does nothing yet leaves nothing undone. A foolish man is always doing, yet much remains to be done." As hypnotherapists, we know one thing that will prevent significant depths of hypnosis from occurring (possibly any hypnosis at all) is if the client "tries" to be hypnotized. In fact, one of the most difficult concepts for people in western culture to understand is that of "doing nothing," yet for hypnosis to be most effective, this is exactly what we need.

A hypnotherapist can greatly enhance his or her success rate by having a plan in place to teach clients or patients how to do nothing. This may sound simple but the fact is that most people have no idea of how to do nothing. Our culture promotes the idea that to be productive we must always be doing something. Without prior "nothingness training" most people will either try to think themselves into hypnosis, or they will try to help in other ways (by listening attentively to the therapist, etc.). Trying is a product of the conscious mind. Hypnosis is achieved by encouraging the conscious mind to step aside so that we can make suggestion to the subconscious mind, without that message first being filtered through the conscious mind. It follows then that anything that would bring the conscious mind back into play will deteriorate trance. Therefore, the person who tries to go into hypnosis will not.

Before inducing hypnosis I ask the person if they are ready to go to that special place within their minds and make the positive changes they have come to me for. Sometimes the reply is "I'll try." I'm sure that most of you who are currently in practice have received that same response at one time or another. How do you answer that statement? Do you say "great lets get started?" If you do, you just shot yourself right in the big toe. Try is the disciple of defeat for a number of reasons. In this particular instance it is because trying requires conscious thought process. My response is… "Oh no, I don't want you to try. What I want you to do is enjoy. Let me do all the work. That's what you paid me for. I want you to take a trip without leaving the farm. I want you to enjoy a massage for the mind. I want you to take a mini mental vacation and leave everything to me." It is important that the person have permission to do absolutely nothing.

THINGS THEY NEED TO KNOW

Your client or patient needs to know what you mean by doing nothing. Here are some analogies and examples that may be useful in explaining it to them. I won't go into the full dialogue that I would use because that would be too lengthy, but you'll get the idea and then you can add your own personal touch.

1. Massage Analogy

Dr. H: Have you ever been for a massage?

Subject: Yes
(Note: If the client says no ask if their spouse, significant other, mother, pet goldfish etc. has ever rubbed or scratched their back for them. You'll likely get a yes from that.)

Dr. H: Well, when you were getting massaged, you didn't stop to think, deltoids relax, now biceps relax, all right now quadriceps relax. You just zoned out and enjoyed the massage and before you knew it you were deeply relaxed. That's what I want you to do today.

2. Beach Analogy

Dr. H: Do you like the beach?

Subject: Yes

Dr. H: I want you to recall the last time you were relaxing peacefully at the beach. You know... when you're lying there in the warmth of the sun drifting away into a dreamy state of mind. There may have been hundreds of people around you talking or playing in the sand but to you they only registered as background noise. If someone were to have said to you, "What did that person next to you just say", you probably couldn't have told them. The sounds around you simply weren't important to you. That's where I want you to go today.

3. Permission NOT to listen with the conscious mind:

Often people think that they must be listening attentively to the therapist to get the message. Here is what I tell them.

Dr. H: I'd like you to know that you don't have to listen to me. If you hear every word I say that is fine so long as you are not "trying" to listen to me. If you don't hear me at all, that is fine too. Your subconscious mind will always hear me. Do you have kids?

Subject: Yes

Dr. H: Well, you know then, that you could be in the deepest sleep at night, and if a car horn beeped out on the street, or someone was talking outside it wouldn't disturb you. But if your child whimpered in the night you'd be out of bed in a flash… right!

Subject: Right

Dr. H: That shows you that your subconscious mind doesn't miss a thing. It's always on duty. So you don't have to listen to me in the conventional sense. Your subconscious mind will always hear me. I want you to simply enjoy this like a mini mental vacation. Just enjoy. Pay no attention to me.

(Note: If the person doesn't have kids I'll go back to an example like the beach. When you're zoned out, all of the people around you become background noise, however, if someone yelled "Shark", you'd jump right up… Right!)

Subject: Agrees

LETTING GO

In western culture we are generally schooled that when something goes wrong we ask what else we can do to make it better. I suggest instead that people ask what they can let go of. What is it that is causing the conflict in your life? What burden are you allowing upon your shoulders? What barriers have you placed in your own path? Rather than adding more clutter, you need to get rid of that baggage. What you need to do is to peel away the layers of the onion until you get to the heart.

We humans love our stuff. It can be material possessions or emotional baggage. Often when our stuff has no purpose in our lives we still hold on to it. I guess that's why you see $40,000.00 cars sitting in a driveway while the person's garage is full of worthless junk that he or she just can't part with. We do cling to our stuff.

The key to opening up to our full potential is in nothingness. It comes by letting go of all that which tethers us to the place in which we find ourselves "stuck". As long as a person thinks he or she has to do something they will find only limited success at best. Rather than taking on tasks within the session, they must accept that it's okay to simply let go and enjoy. Encourage them to let go and allow their imagination to be their guide. Like when they were children and a cardboard box could easily become a car, a train, or a rocket to the moon. That is the part of them that will give them great power. Prepare your client to do nothing, and everything they ever dreamed up will become available to them.

Chapter 9

Children and Hypnotherapy

When working with children it is even more important than with adults to establish trust and rapport. As odd as it may seem to those of us in therapeutic profession, often those unfamiliar with hypnosis/hypnotherapy still have some pretty strange ideas about what we do. As you are probably aware, the thing that will most often prevent someone from going into hypnosis is fear. Why would we expect children then to react with greater confidence than an adult? After all, a child meeting a strange adult authority figure (therapist/counselor/Dr.) for the first time is bound to be a bit nervous. It is essential then that any child that comes to you feel completely comfortable. If the parents bring the child to you kicking and screaming you won't get much accomplished.

FIRST STEP

The process of preparing the child begins when the parent(s) first contacts you. After obtaining general preliminary information (name, contact info, reason for call, etc.), I make it a point to ask the parent if the child has been told that he or she may be coming for hypnotherapy and if so, exactly what the child has been told. This is important because I will handle my first contact with the child differently if the child has been advised that he or she will be seeing a "Hypnotherapist."

If the child (especially if the child is under about 12) has not been told that the parent is planning to take the child for hypnotherapy I generally will suggest that they do not mention the word hypnosis at that time. I suggest that they simply tell their child that he/she will be visiting someone who can help them accomplish their goals, or that will help them to maximize their potential, or something along those lines. It is important that the child get to know and feel comfortable with you one step at a time. The idea of "hypnosis" should be introduced on the child's timetable, not yours or the parents.

FIRST VISIT

I always advise the parents well in advance about what to expect on the first visit, and why. That way it is not a surprise to the parents when I sit down on the floor with the child for a game of checkers or connect four. "Rapport" is first on the agenda of things to be accomplished. On the child's first visit, (and in some situations on the second), I do no hypnotherapy per se. We sit and talk. We get to know each other. During that "informal intake" I am able to put together a picture of what the child wants and needs, and what will motivate the child to make those positive changes. At the same time, the child begins to feel comfortable with me.

When the child is ready to move on to the actual hypnotherapy, I may or may not use the word hypnosis depending on the child. If I elect to define what we are doing in terms of hypnosis I begin by telling the child that kids have a wonderful and natural talent. They have the ability to do something far better than any adult and that it is they have the power of imagination. I'll say something like… "Would you like to have some fun? I'd like to show you just how very powerful your imagination is. Let me show you something really neat. First though, I just need your promise that for the next few minutes you'll pretend that anything that I tell you can really happen. Will you do that for me?" When he or she agrees I'll do something simple like an eye-lock, or hand lock. The child invariably is thrilled and amused with the results. Then I'll say to the child… "Did you know that your mind was so powerful? It's your mind that made that possible, not me!" Then I'll introduce the term hypnosis by saying something like… "Do you know what we just did? We actually did hypnosis." Did you know that hypnosis was so easy or so much fun? By this time he or she has accepted hypnosis as something pleasant and interesting. We can now proceed with the child's acceptance and cooperation.

If the child knows in advance of coming that he or she will be experiencing hypnosis, I begin by asking them what they think hypnosis is, and how he or she feels about hypnosis. This gives me an opportunity to discover any fears or misconceptions and address them. I explain that we all go into hypnosis quite often without even recognizing it as hypnosis (and then I give them some examples, like spacing out in front of the TV or daydreaming). Then I proceed basically in the same way that I would in the previous scenario. I give them the opportunity to experience the "fun" of hypnosis. This increases their level of excitement, anticipation, and compliance.

With some children, I never use the word hypnosis at all. I simply tell them that we are going to play some imagination games. I say that we're going to have some fun while at the same time opening up that powerful imagination of theirs, letting it work for them in accomplishing their goal(s). Many children complete successful therapy without even identifying it with hypnosis. What we call the process is unimportant. The main concern is getting results in whatever format is comfortable for the child.

TRUST

It is important that the child know that you are working for them and that he or she can trust you. A therapist needs to make it a point to let the child know that he or she cares about what the child's goals are. I will often say, "I know what mom and dad want you to accomplish. I want to know what you want to accomplish. I let the child know that even though mom and dad brought them, that he or she is the person that I am there for. It is important that the child know that you are not there simply to carry out the parent's wishes. The child must know that you are there to benefit him or her.

POINTERS

The following are some pointers that you might find helpful.

Don't be "clinical." Have a pleasant and friendly demeanor. Work with children on their own level. I literally position myself in a way that is non-intimidating to the child. If I'm going to play a game with the child I will usually put the game on the floor and get down on the floor with the child. Proceed within the child's timeframe. Those of you with children know that children do not have the same priorities or sense of time that adults have. Successful therapy depends on working on the child's timetable, not yours or the child's parents. I have turned away cases where the parents have had a specific and unrealistic timetable they wanted to impose on the child. Let the child know that you are working for them and no one else.

It is not important that the child know that you are using hypnosis. What is important is that you have the child's trust and acceptance. If the child wants to work with the therapist, he or she will have success. And by the way... praise the child. Give the child the inspiration and a reason to want to return and continue working toward his or her goal(s). I have a basket of inexpensive games and toys in my therapy room that I let the child pick from as a reward for a job well done at the end of the session.

REWARD

Kids are great to work with. A therapist can find great satisfaction in the proud and joyful smile of a child who realizes his or her potential, and in the joy of a parent who realizes the prospect of a better and happier life for their child. In all likelihood, the therapist will experience equal joy to that of the child and his or her parents when they help that child reach his or her goal.

CHAPTER 10

MEN, WOMEN, AND HYPNOSIS

PROCESSING INFORMATION

Everyone knows (unless they grew up under an eggplant) that men and women process information differently. Irrespective of the "pop-psychology" of the last few decades where some therapists and researchers would have you believe that most male/female differences are primarily acquired through socialization, the fact is that there are social, biological, and evolutionary reasons why men and women process information differently. To attribute these vast differences to socialization alone (or for that matter even in great part) is pure nonsense. The idea that male/female, behavior is primarily a result of socialization is usually a perspective advocated by people who have a particular political and social agenda they wish to promote.

Nature has given men and women their unique physical differences to assure the continuation of the human race. This is equally true of our psychological development as a species. Through centuries of evolution, men acquired the ability to focus intensely on one objective while women developed the complementary ability of multi-tasking. Men were the hunters and warriors. This necessitated having the ability to remain very focused and directed. Men acquired superior spatial perception needed for navigating through the woods while hunting or for traveling when going off to war or to scout for game. Women on the other hand gathered food and other materials for the home, watched the children, and cooked and cared for the immediate needs of the family.

Through necessity women acquired a greater ability to multi-task. It would be foolish to assume that modern pop-culture could suddenly erase what has evolved naturally over hundreds of thousands of years.

Anyone who is married knows what I'm talking about… Men and women process information differently! For most men, give us one thing at a time to do and we'll do it well. We tend to stay focused and on track (most of the time). We generally do not do as well working with multiple tasks simultaneously. Women on the other hand can cook dinner, balance the checkbook, watch the kids, and talk on the phone at the same time. They, however, usually find it more difficult to focus on one thing without interjecting peripheral topics. Neither one is better. Men and women are simply wired differently.

Through this evolutionary process the brain function of men and women has evolved differently as well. Generally speaking, the difference is this… women use both hemispheres of the brain at the same time. Men on the other hand use only one hemisphere of the brain at a time. This, in fact, is what gives women the greater ability to multi-task. It is also what sometimes prevents them from staying on subject. Men on the other hand usually have greater focus but often are uncomfortable with multiple tasks.

COMMUNICATION

Women also tend to be more communicative and take greater interest in peripheral information. If you put two women who have never met together on a train from Philadelphia to New York, by the time the two get to New York they will likely know each others entire life story. By the same token you can have two men working in the same office for ten years who may not even know the names of each other's spouse or kids. Men and women are wired differently.

GENDER SPECIFIC THERAPY

Long ago I noticed the difference in how men and women process hypnotic suggestion. Although one should not assume the differences to be concrete in all cases (there are exceptions to every rule), generally I have found certain things to be true. [NOTE: Surprisingly, this topic, to the best of my knowledge, receives little to no attention in hypnotherapy training programs. Perhaps such topics are just not "politically correct."] An understanding of the differences between men and women and the way in which they each process information can make a world of differences when structuring productive sessions.

IN THERAPY

Many times over the years I have had students and fellow practitioners alike ask me if I could figure out why they were having success with some people and not with others, even while using basically the same therapeutic model. I frequently suggest that they check to see if there is a correlation between their successes, and the gender of the people that they have had success with. Although these differences in results can sometimes be from individual personality differences, I find more often that the therapist is having good results with one gender and not as good with the other. This occurs because the therapist has not taken into consideration the differences in how males and females process the information provided by the therapist. They often treat men and women the same. That is a mistake. In case anyone out there hasn't noticed, men and women are different. That's what makes it nice for dancing (among other things).

MEN AND HYPNOTHERAPY

As a general rule of thumb you will get better results with men by keeping things simple and more specific. It is usually better to select a limited number of suggestions that have been carefully prioritized, and then compound, compound, compound. With men, less is often more. It is not the length of the session or the number of suggestions that will bring success but rather the quality and relevance of the suggestions made.

Remember, the subconscious mind is like the little kid in us. If you were to sit with a little boy, and make dozens of complex statements to him, it would not take long before he would be squirming in his seat. He would quickly reach a saturation point and be looking for a door out. By the same token, dozens of complex and/or flowery suggestions will often cause a man to quickly reach a saturation point. He will be looking for a way out. The way out will usually be to bring himself out of hypnosis, or to simply begin rejecting the over-saturation of suggestions. As well, you can reach a point of diminishing return simply keeping someone in hypnosis too long (especially males). More is not always better. With men, keep it simple, direct, and focused on the suggestions that have a high level of immediate relevance. One other "suggestion"… In my opinion it is most often a mistake to give male clients or patients lots of triggers or cues, to work with [e.g.: squeezing fingers together, switching chairs etc. to change the setting in which a behavior is occurring, snapping a rubber band that is placed around his wrist, swinging a chicken over their head while reciting affirmations (just kidding about the chicken), and so forth.] Very quickly the little boy within will interpret these "tasks" as being an effort and a pain in the posterior region. The suggestion(s) therefore will have no durability, and the triggers will be either rejected, and/or not utilized.

WOMEN

Women seem to respond favorably, to more intricate suggestions than do men. Again remember, in hypnosis you are talking to the little kid within the person. In most cases, a young girl would be more willing to sit quietly and enjoy more intricate tasks or stories than would a young boy of similar age. Women may also respond to metaphor in a more positive and significant way than men. As well, women seem to have a longer duration before reaching a saturation point with the hypnotic process. Because of their ability to multi-task suggestions that mix practical and emotional components are more appropriate for women than with men. Triggers and cues like the ones mentioned above often work well with women. Women more easily accept such ritual.

THE RIGHT TOOL

In hypnotherapy one size does not fit all. That is why I'm not particularly fond of patter scripts. There are many things that must be considered in designing a therapy. Personality, age, perception (based on the individuals life experience) are but a few. Gender is always an important issue because it has significance in ways that surpass that of life experience and socialization. There are biological, and evolutionary factors at work. Gender determines to a significant extent how that client/patient will process the information that the therapist provides.

If working with a woman the therapist must also work with the little girl within her. The therapist might ask him or herself what things a little girl might relate and respond best to. If the therapist is working with a man, he or she is also working with the little boy within him. The therapist should consider what things a little boy might best relate and respond to. By following this format the therapist can use the power of human nature to increase the impact of his or her sessions and to empower the client or patient.

Chapter 11

Session Work

CONDUCTING AN EFFECTIVE SMOKE CESSATION SESSION

Although demand has been decreasing in recent years due to a smaller percentage of the population using tobacco products, it still makes up a significant portion of many practitioners' practice. As well, smoke cessation is one of the simpler therapies making it a great place for new therapists to cut their teeth.

PRE-SESSION MOTIVATION

Since many smokers have a love-hate relationship with tobacco thorough preparation, including a significant amount of waking hypnotic suggestion (during the pre-talk) is essential. In fact, most of your success or failure with a smoker will be determined during the pre-talk and preparation stages.

The most important thing to accomplish in the pre-talk is to overcome any fears or concerns the person may harbor about giving up tobacco. These may include, fear of gaining weight after giving up tobacco, fear of withdraw, or simply fear of letting go of that crutch… being without the "friend" that they have thought tobacco to be. Also most smokers began smoking in adolescence. The majority of the time they started to be "part of the group," or to be "cool." Although logically they usually know that they no longer need tobacco to be accepted (to the contrary smoking is no longer accepted by the majority as chic), the child within, the subconscious mind, still holds on to the that idea. Also keep in mind that aversion therapy rarely works long-term. It is far better to approach smoke cessation from the standpoint of reward. What does the person expect to get by becoming a non-smoker? How will he or she benefit? You'll get a lot more mileage from a positive approach. Always dangle a carrot rather than imposing a punishment.

Below you will find some approaches that you might find helpful. These suggestions address some of the most rudimentary aspects of therapy involved when working with a future non-smoker.

FEAR OF GAINING WEIGHT

One of the most common fears is that of weight gain after the person gives up smoking. It is important to alleviate that fear before you begin the hypnotic process. If you do not, the person may simply refuse your suggestions out of fear that they may gain weight. There are a number of ways to overcome this fear and circumvent that obstacle. Here are a couple of useful tips.

In the pre-talk I mention to the person that the people who come to me to stop smoking have an added advantage. I tell the person that not only will he or she not pick up another bad habit like overeating that could lead to weight gain but that they can even lose some weight if they would like to. [Note: if the person is exceedingly thin to begin with weight gain may not be an issue. You need to determine that in the intake.] I tell the person that the same general area of the brain that is stimulated by nicotine is the same area that is stimulated by sugars and complex carbohydrates that are converted by the body to sugars. I go on to say that the reason that some people go from smoking to eating either candy or carbohydrates is because the brain is looking for the stimulation once provided by the nicotine. I convince them that their subconscious mind has the power to simply shut off that need. Because of this they will not move from one bad habit to another. I tell them that I can even program a little weight loss into the session so that they can lose weight when giving up tobacco if they choose. Once in trance I simply suggest that when I count backwards from three to one, when I touch them on the forehead, or whatever mechanism I decide to tell them that I will use, their subconscious mind will erase the need for the input of sweetness once supplied by tobacco. I tell them that they are now free from that previous negative programming and that they now have the ability to maintain their current weight or to lose weight if they so desire. In any event there will be no substitute negative habit like unhealthy eating. I reinforce that they have chosen to reward themselves with a healthy body.

Another method that I have found works quite well is this. I suggest that if ever (not when ever) he or she is tempted to use a tobacco product, instantly a "dryness" will begin to form in their mouth. It will grow stronger and stronger and they will desire only cool refreshing water. When they drink the water, even the smallest amount, their mouth will feel cool and refreshed. Any desire for tobacco will be washed away, and they will feel wonderfully proud that they are in control of their lives.

FEAR OF WITHDRAWAL

It is the fear of impending withdrawal, more than the actuality of future withdrawal that can prevent a successful session. For this reason the client or patient must in advance perceive that withdrawal can be avoided. If the person's belief structure is there then your post-hypnotic suggestions for smoke cessation will be more readily accepted by the subconscious mind. As previously discussed, this must be accomplished in great part in the pre-talk. The following dialogue is one approach that I have found to be effective with those concerned about nicotine withdrawal.

Therapist: You know that we all have great power within our minds that often goes untapped, wouldn't you agree? (Be sure to be nodding your head "yes" as you ask the question)

Client/Patient: (Agrees)

Therapist: Well, you know that we can easily tap into that power through the use of hypnosis. That's why you are here, right? (Nodding yes again as you ask the question)

Client/Patient: (Agrees)

Therapist: You have been putting poisons and toxins into your body with those cigarettes for a while now, but the interesting thing is that from the moment you become a non-smoker, your body will begin to heal. Isn't that great? (Nodding yes again as you ask the question)

Client/Patient: (Agrees)

Therapist: Your mind also has the power to ignore any residual cravings, like those commonly called withdrawal, during the healing process. Hypnosis can help you in the same way that a decongestant helps you when you have a cold. When you have a cold you feel lousy. If you take some cold medicine your head clears up and you feel much better right? (Nodding "yes" again as you ask the question). Well, hypnosis can work in much the same way helping you to feel great while your body continues to heal and get rid of any residual toxins. Your subconscious mind has the power to actually ignore withdrawal. If you feel great, and you are unaware of any cravings, isn't that kind of the same thing? If you simply loan me your imagination together we can make that happen very easily. You'd like that wouldn't you? (Nodding "yes" again as you ask the question)

Client/Patient: (Agrees)

It is important that you have the person's compliance and agreement throughout the process of this waking hypnotic suggestion. With each yes, or nod of their head, you are further establishing that concept to be real.

Once in the hypnotic process, you can simply suggest that you are now erasing any discomfort, including symptoms of withdrawal, from the blackboard of their mind. If the person is visual, you can have them picture the word withdrawal on the blackboard of their mind and then erase it.

Another method to eliminate the fear of withdrawal is similar to a basic pain management technique. For the visual person you can have them imagine a small switch at the base of his or her brain. Suggest that this switch is the switch responsible for turning on and off the discomfort associated with withdrawal. Have them turn the switch off and securely lock the switch in the off position. This works best when you have them turn the switch to the off position and than nod to you when they have done so. Their active participation adds great power to this technique.

WITHOUT THE "FRIEND"

Often smokers look at tobacco as a friend. They and their nicotine have shared stress, happiness, coffee, alcohol, and breaks from chores. I often suggest that in the past, he or she has looked at tobacco as a friend. I suggest that from this moment forward they accept the complete understanding that tobacco was never really their friend. After all, a friend would not lead you into sickness or death.

There is an interesting component involving the idea of tobacco relaxing someone that can be addressed with waking hypnotic suggestion during the pre-talk. This too will alleviate fear and/or concern on the part of the client or patient regarding their letting go of the tobacco habit. We know that tobacco is a stimulant. It won't relax anyone. I have found that it often comes down to the old chicken and the egg idea of which came first? Here is where you can help the person shift gears and gain a new perspective. You might say something like this: You know that tobacco is a stimulant. It doesn't relax anyone, right? (Nod yes and get their agreement). Did you ever stop to think that maybe you didn't start taking a break to have a cigarette, but that you actually went out for a cigarette so that you could get a break? (Again nodding yes and getting their agreement) My experience has been that the vast majority of people will reply with something like, "you know, I never thought of it like that." Assure them that they really can have the break without the excuse of having a cigarette. They are in power not the cigarettes.

PART OF THE GROUP

Most people began smoking (usually as adolescents) to be part of the group. They wanted to be cool and to fit in. Helping your client or patient recognize that their acceptance was not then, nor is it now dependent on tobacco will go a long way in helping them to give up smoking. Today smokers are no longer thought of as cool. To the contrary, smokers are often thought to be lacking in common sense and intelligence. You can help them to see that they can show their great level of intelligence, pride, and wisdom through becoming a non-smoker. Today it is the smoker who is the outsider, often thought to be less intelligent. By becoming a non-smoker others will instantly view that person in a more positive light. I often suggest that smokers today are often forced to go outside or to another area to smoke… It's like they have their own leper's colony. After all… being part of a group is one thing but most people would prefer not to be part of a leper's colony.

CONNECTION TO OTHER ACTIVITIES

Often smokers connect smoking to other activities such as eating, driving, having a drink, or with their morning coffee. It is important to break that connection so as not to have that connection trigger the person back to smoking once you have helped them to stop.

Find out during the intake at what times or during what situations is the person most likely to smoke. Once you have established what these situations are you can help them to break the connection between smoking and those activities. Let's say the person tells you that they usually smoke with their morning coffee and when they are in the car. Your suggestion might go something like this.

"In a moment I'm going to call upon your powerful subconscious mind to break the connection between smoking and other activities… especially between smoking while driving in the car, and especially with your morning coffee. In fact there will be no time that smoking will be desirable to you. You will feel great… proud and free! Here's how we'll do it. In a moment I'm going to count backwards from 3 to 1. When I reach the number 1, I'll touch you on the forehead. At that very instant, your subconscious mind, working on your behalf, will simply break the connection between tobacco and other activities. From that moment forward you are in charge. Tobacco will no longer have any hold on you.

There will be no time that tobacco will be desirable to you. If you start with the idea of wanting that to happen it will happen easily. Here we go… 3---- 2---- 1 (as I touch his or her forehead I repeat 6 or 8 times "Your very powerful mind has broken the connection between tobacco and other activities. There is no time that tobacco is desirable to you. You're in charge.) "

RECURRENCE

One other trigger that can send people back to smoking is the sight or smell of tobacco. One very effective way to neutralize that trigger is to utilize the sight and smell of tobacco as positive triggers to help the person remain a non-smoker. I often use this suggestion. "From this moment forward, whenever you see tobacco products, or smell tobacco products or the smoke from tobacco products something amazing and wonderful will happen. From this moment forward, the sight or smell of tobacco products will actually increase your determination to remain a proud, wise, and intelligent, non-smoker. The sight or smell of tobacco repels you away from that disgusting habit. You are in charge. No longer do you turn control of your life over to a disgusting cancer stick. You are a proud non-smoker."

REWARDS

The most important consideration (as in many therapies) is to establish a reward system. In the intake you must establish specifically what it is that the person expects to gain by being a non-smoker. During the session you must reinforce that reward system. For example if a client or patient says that they fear dying young, or being ill throughout their life, ask them why specifically that is a concern. The person might say they would like to be able to enjoy seeing their child grow up and graduate college. If that is the case a suggestion like: You've decided to reward yourself with a healthy body... To have both a longer life and a better quality of life, able to enjoy your children, and all of the other wonderful things that you desire for many, many, years to come. No longer do you allow tobacco to rob you of those wonderful years.

The most powerful tool that you have in the vast majority of therapies is a well-structured reward system that will inspire and motivate the client or patient. Recognizing that the subconscious mind adheres more strongly to positive suggestion, it is easy to see the value in a positive reward system.

BE SELECTIVE

If a person is not ready to stop smoking they will not. You must be confident of their desire to stop and of their level of motivation before you begin with the hypnotic process. If they are attempting to stop smoking for any other reason than their own true desire to stop you would be best advised not to schedule their session(s). The worst advertisement for your practice is a dissatisfied client or patient.

HEALTHY WEIGHT LOSS WITH HYPNOSIS

Hypnosis can be a powerful tool in the battle against the bulge. It is important however to have knowledge about how the body works with regard to weight loss in order to assure that your client or patient will lose weight in a healthy way. Not all weight loss is conducive to health and wellness.

You want people to both lose weight and feel great. If they lose weight and feel like crap, it isn't doing much for them or for your reputation.

Many of the patter scripts and suggestions for weight loss that I have heard fail to take into account fundamental health factors in losing weight. I have always been very involved in physical fitness training. In the past, I have worked as a physical fitness trainer and consultant and I still keep up a rigorous personal training program. I incorporate this knowledge into my weight loss sessions so that my clients/patients can lose weight and feel great. In order to accomplish this, it is essential that a hypnotist or hypnotherapist providing weight loss as one of his or her services be knowledgeable in this area.

EATING LESS IS NOT THE ANSWER

Most people think that the less someone eats, the more fat they will lose. This is not necessarily true. Although a person's intake of calories and his or her corresponding level of activity (burning calories) have an effect on weight, they are only part of the equation. Just as important is how and what you eat, and how you exercise. The best way to lose weight is with a healthy "eating plan" of nutritious foods (often with more, but smaller meals, eaten throughout the day). Often six small meals will facilitate weight loss better than one or two larger meals. Sound crazy?... read on and you'll see why this is true. Healthy eating along with a reasonable exercise plan will virtually assure a shapelier body and a feeling of health and vitality... not just a loss of pounds.

WHAT HAPPENS WHEN YOU EAT TOO LITTLE

Those who assume that healthy weight loss can be accomplished by focusing on suggestion that a person can simply eat less, or avoid snacks, may be setting themselves up for disappointment and setting up their client or patient for disaster. Let me explain what happens when someone eats too little in an attempt to lose weight.

The human body expects and/or needs a certain volume of fuel (food) in order to complete the tasks and functions that the person demands from it. This of course varies with a person's level of activity and overall physical condition. When a person's body doesn't receive an adequate supply of fuel, his or her body presumes itsself to be starving. As a natural survival response his or her body essentially says… "I am not getting enough fuel so I will need to slow down the consumption of fuel." It does so by slowing the metabolic rate. When this happens, there are residual effects. As the metabolic rate slows, calories are consumed at a slower rate making it even more difficult to lose weight. Even more importantly, in an attempt to hoard fuel, the person's body will hold on to, and even bloat fat cells, in anticipation of starvation. The body will then begin to break down muscle tissue as it's alternate source of fuel. Remember too, as the person's metabolic rate drops, a loss of energy is experienced making it even more difficult for the person to find motivation to exercise. This increases the downward spiral taking the person farther from his or her goal for weight loss. Since muscle weighs more than fat, the person may lose some weight by eating less, but the loss is more likely to be the muscle that he or she wanted to keep rather than the fat they wanted to lose. Muscle consumes calories every moment of the day in an attempt to maintain itself. The more muscle mass, the quicker you can lose weight and the more energetic you feel. For healthy weight loss it is important not only to maintain, but also to increase muscle mass and density.

WHERE DO YOUR EATING HABITS COME FROM

Our relationship with food is formed very early in our lives. When we were babies and our parents held, comforted, and fed us it created a mental connection between food, and love, security and friendship. This connection has no basis in reality, but it does have a strong subconscious "perceived reality." For some people this connection is stronger than for others. As we grow older this connection is reinforced (if you're good, mommy/daddy will give you a cookie etc.). When we reach the dating age, where does a guy take his best girl? To dinner of course! In ours, as well as many other societies, food plays a big role in our socialization. Similarly to Pavlov's dog (creating a mental connection between salivating and the ringing of a bell), we create a connection between food, and love, security and friendship. It is done through what we call "waking hypnotic suggestion." This is why when many people are sad, stressed, happy, or lonely (and for virtually any other strong emotion), they turn to food. They are looking for security, love, and friendship. Where do they find that friend? They find it in the refrigerator or pantry of course!

CHANGING BEHAVIOR AND PERCEPTION

Part of a successful hypnotherapy weight loss program involves breaking the connection between food, and love, security, and friendship. This breaks too the cycle of pacifying emotional highs or lows with food. A new relationship with food can then be established making it much easier to lose weight in a healthy way. This needs to be accomplished in a way that brings health and energy. It is not in a person's best interest to simply have them lose pounds by eating less. The result may be a lighter fat person (lost muscle and gained fat).

Behaviors, habits, and emotions as we know are housed in the subconscious mind. It stands to reason then that the most expeditious way to modify such behaviors is at the subconscious level. The simplest and most direct way to speak to the subconscious mind of course is through hypnosis. A person's relationship with food was formed there, and it can be most effectively changed at a subconscious level. The first step to a new relationship with food isn't excessive exercise, starvation, or eating things that the person hates. A healthier happier life begins with reprogramming the person's relationship with food and with exercise.

IMPORTANT AREAS OF SUGGESTION

Pre-talk:

As with many therapies success or failure may very well be determined in the pre-talk. One important factor in the pre-talk is what I call the weight loss threshold. Most people assume that they will have to make huge changes in both diet and exercise in order to loose weight. This may simply not be so. Most people are not as far away from that line, or threshold, as they think. It is important to assure your person that he or she may already be right up to that important threshold. He or she may only need to make minor changes in diet and exercise in order to bump over to the "lose weight" side of the line. This knowledge will provide the confidence and the incentive they need to make the commitment to a healthier life. With this knowledge the job doesn't seem so insurmountable and the person will feel more assured that he or she can do it!

SUGGESTION

The following are some areas that I recommend you cover within sessions for weight loss.

How they look:

Some people will tell you that they want to lose weight strictly for health reasons. This may be true to an extent, but virtually everyone wants to look better too. There are times when a person may feel shy or vain in saying that he or she wants to look better. The fact is when you look good and you feel good your self-esteem grows and therefore one's perception of life in general grows brighter. If he or she is a visual person, have them see themselves as they have chosen to be. Suggest that they look healthy and fit, suggest that because of this decision their clothes fit better, as well others see the positive changes in them etc.

Easy and pleasant:

Suggest that starving and those difficult diets are not necessary. A healthy eating plan made up of many small meals during the day keeps them comfortable and content. They prevent the body from anticipating starvation and therefore reduce fat cells while they elevate energy levels. Continue by reinforcing the idea of "small meals" and "greater energy".

How they feel:

Almost every person wants to have more energy and vitality. Assure them that the wonderful decision that they have made will lead to greater energy and the ability to enjoy life to the fullest. Everything is better when you have a healthy body. Suggest how great they will feel as others see the positive changes in them.

Exercise:

Many people look at exercise as work. Suggest that when he or she thinks of exercise that his or her mind will go immediately to that feeling of health and vitality that you get from exercise. I always ask what physical activity the person has most enjoyed and I use that feeling to enable them to reconstruct a positive sensation about physical activity.

What better gift:

Many people reward themselves with food. Change the reward system! Suggest that they reward themselves with a more attractive body, energy, and vitality. What better gift than both a longer life and a better quality of life.

Healthy body erases aches and pains:

When a person's body is strong and healthy, there is a reduction in discomfort due to minor aches and pains. This too may provide inspiration that will please the subconscious mind.

GIVE THEM A NEW LEASE ON LIFE

If you take into consideration the way the body reacts to food and to exercise, you can put your clients/patients on the path to a healthier and happier life. Having them lose weight is not enough, especially if it comes at the expense of his or her health. This is especially significant when he or she is unable to maintain that lower weight due to a slowed metabolic rate. Give your clients/patients more than a lower reading on the scale. Give them the health and vitality that should go with it.

CONDUCTING AN EFFECTIVE STRESS MANAGEMENT SESSION

WHAT CAUSES STRESS? The answer is… Just about anything! Chicken soup can cause stress if you happen to hate chicken soup. Circumstances that cause feelings of stress vary from person to person. What one person considers pleasant, another may very well find extremely stressful. For example: I live near Philadelphia. Like any busy area there are a lot highways and fast moving traffic. I always tell people that if you drive in Philadelphia or New York, you have to drive like you know where you are going even if you do not. My parents will not drive when they come here to visit me. It's far too stressful for them. They live in a rural area. There are far fewer cars and everyone moves more slowly. Personally, I can't stand driving in areas like that. People often go 35 miles per hour in 55 mile per hour zones, wait long after traffic lights have turned to green to move, and essentially drive like they have all day to get to the end of the street. I find it far more stressful to drive under those conditions than I do in Philly or New York City traffic. Since different stressors affect every person in a different way, there is no blanket formula for alleviating feelings of stress. As a therapist, it is essential to find out what triggers the feelings of stress within each person and address those triggers.

MANAGEMENT VS. REDUCTION

First of all, there is no such thing as a stress reduction technique. Short of convincing a person to move into a cave in the mountains he or she will always encounter stressors throughout life. A more accurate term is "Stress Management." The key to stress management is to understand that we all have the power to keep stress on the outside where the stressors usually come from rather than internalizing them.

I was given a coffee mug as a gift that has this definition of stress written on it… "Stress: The confusion created when one's mind overrides the body's basic desire to choke the living S_ _ T (poop) out of some A __-hole who desperately deserves it." [I cleaned up the language written on the mug]. My mug, however, makes a very valid point. In ancient times if someone threatened you, you either ran, or you clubbed him over the head. This is an instinct provided by Mother Nature for our safety and survival. This instinct is called "fight or flight". The problem today is that societal requirements usually prevent us from exercising either of these natural defensive responses. As an example… If someone's boss were to yell at him or her, and the person were to run out of the building, he or she would probably lose their job. As well, if he or she clubbed his or her boss over the head with the nearest chair, they would lose their job and most likely end up in jail. Most often in modern society it is impossible to respond with the natural instincts of "fight or flight." It is impossible to run and it is illegal to clobber the person who is the source of your frustration. The Fight or Flight instinct being effectively neutered stress will manifest. Certain amounts of stress can serve a useful purpose. It can put us on alert and make us more vigilant. Anything over and above small levels of stress can be destructive.

STRESS MANAGEMENT

The most important component in helping a person to effectively manage stress is to discover what stimuli most powerfully triggers his or her negative response to stressors. [You must consider as well that the effects of stress are cumulative. What occurs most often is what I call the "straw that broke the camel's back syndrome." Each subsequent stressor makes the one(s) that came before and/or after, more powerful.]

As with most therapies involving hypnosis, the key to a productive stress management session is a well-structured intake and pre-talk. Once (through the intake) you have gathered the relevant information needed to construct suggestions specific to "that person's motivators" you begin the person's preparation process. In the pre-talk I strive to increase the person's confidence in their ability to succeed. If the person believes that he or she has the power to keep stress on the outside instead of internalizing it… they will do so successfully! I usually say something like this to the person during the preparation process.

"You know that there will always be situations around us that generate stress… Right? (person affirms). We can't always control what goes on around us, but you realize that you truly have complete power to control what you internalize… don't you? (I nod my head yes as the person affirms/agrees) In actuality, no one, and nothing has any power over us other than what we give it. In most cases people internalize stress because no one has ever showed or told them that they actually have the power to keep stress on the outside where it can't disturb you… Wouldn't you agree? (person affirms). I'm simply going to help put you in the driver's seat. You can easily take back control of you're life from stress. Your subconscious mind will simply take back control by accepting only those things that are productive and beneficial to you. It is like a gatekeeper. Humans, often act like herd animals. If one person gets a Tickle Me Elmo or a Furby, everyone has got to have theirs too. Six months later the thing is on the shelf collecting dust, and the person who bought it is wondering why they ever bought it. People often take on stress in the same way. I'm sure that you have noticed that when a person is in a room and others are acting stressed, displaying signs of anxiousness, frustration, or worry, that person usually feels compelled to join the club and become anxious too. He or she generally feels that if everyone else is stressed, they should be too. Wouldn't you agree that this is often the case? (person affirms) Have you ever asked yourself why you have to get stressed-out simply because others do, or because you might be in the midst of a bad situation? Did you ever notice that you are at your best when you are peaceful, calm, and relaxed? (person affirms) You feel better, you make better decisions, and you handle problems with greater wisdom. You've noticed that too, haven't you? (person affirms) Well, you have the power to do that all of the time. I'm going to provide you with the tools that you need to tap into that power. I'm going to give you a simple mechanism that will allow you to expel stress and keep it on the outside where it belongs. You've had this ability all along. I'm simply going to show you how to use it. I'm going to give you a tool that will enable you to tap into your ability to remain centered and calm. You'd like that wouldn't you?" (person affirms)

IN PLACE

Once I have prepared the person and he or she has agreed that keeping stress on the outside is something that is available to them, everything is in place. I then set out to do two things within the hypnotherapy session. I work to change the perception that the person has regarding how he or she relates to stressful situations thereby creating a frame of mind where the person gives less power to stressful situations, And I give the person a trigger mechanism that they can use to expel any stress that they may take on in the future. This is important because it puts the power in the person's hands. As well, the power they have taken back in their life grows stronger each time they use the trigger(s) provided thereby increasing both their confidence and their faith that they can continue to do it. It is sort of like exercising a muscle. The more you use it the stronger it gets. In very short order this "practiced behavior" becomes who they are. [NOTE: I am a big believer in the power of practiced behavior. Often people wait for "Inspiration" to hit them and motivate them to make a change. I believe that the behavior precedes the feeling. With anything that you practice you become more proficient. If you practiced baseball every day you would become a good baseball player. If you practiced carpentry every day, you would become a good carpenter. If you practiced knitting every day you would become good at knitting. Behaviors and perceptions are no different. If you practice confident behavior you will likely become confident. If you practice being peaceful and calm, you will become more peaceful and calm. In essence, you become what you practice to be.]

TRIGGERS

I usually incorporate "breaths" into stress management triggers. This is simply because taking a deep breath, or sigh, is a natural response for releasing stress. There are a number of things that you can attach to the breath. Following is a brief description of two (of many) that I often use.

While in hypnosis I have the person rid him or herself of stress by blowing all stress and negativity into a balloon (I usually count off ten breaths for them). Then I have them observe the negativity contained in the balloon. I then have the person release the balloon and watch it drift away. I have them notice that the farther it drifts, the more they smile, the happier they feel, the prouder they feel, etc. Then we simply let the balloon disappear and along with it, all stress and negativity. I then suggest that anytime stress or tension tries to "invade them," they will take a deep breath in, close their eyes, and blow any stress or negativity into the balloon with one deep breath. He or she will then simply watch the balloon drift away carrying all stress and negativity with it. I also repeat the suggestions that the farther it drifts, the more they smile, the happier they feel, the prouder they feel, and so on. For those people that are less visual, I give a physical trigger. I may have them simply throw the stress away like a wad of paper. Here is an easy trigger that I use. I have them take a deep breath in and close their eyes. I have the person close one hand tightly. Then I have them open their hand, releasing the stress. I have them do that 5 or 10 times with the suggestion that each time they open their hand, casting out the stress, the more they will smile, the happier they feel, the prouder they feel, etc. I suggest that any time they detect stress trying to invade them, they will repeat this action and the stress will vanish.

Another method I use is to have them construct a magic bubble around them. I tell them that this magical bubble has fascinating properties. This bubble will repel all negativity while at the same time allowing anything positive (love, humor, etc.) to filter through easily. I then provide them with a trigger to bring back and/or strengthen this protective bubble whenever they feel the need to.

STRESS AND EXPECTATION

A very important area that I find many therapists sometime are not addressing is the subject of "Expectation."

A significant percentage of stress related problems are the result of a person's expectations of both themselves and of others. Often these expectations are unrealistic. When a person harbors these expectations, and the expectations are not fulfilled, internal emotional and mental stress may often result. I have a personal life philosophy that "I don't expect anything from anybody." By expecting nothing, everything I receive is a gift and I am never disappointed. I'm not saying that we should not strive to do better in our lives by setting goals and by being diligent in achieving those goals. I'm not saying that we shouldn't set standards for our children as well as for ourselves. I am simply saying that the goals we set for ourselves must be realistic. As well, we must help our clients and patients understand that they have no control over others and therefore cannot expect others to live up to their image of how, what, and who, the other person should be. We are not in this world to live up to the expectations of others nor are others in this world to live up to our expectations. Unfortunately, we (as a species) do expect others to behave and to think as we do.

As hypnotherapists we know that what the mind perceives as real, is real to that individual within the context of that person's perception of the world. Because each person perceives the world differently, expectation of others is often a setup for stress related problems and disappointments… especially when we expect others to fulfill our expectation of how they should think and act.

In order to help clients or patients to cope with stress it is often productive to work with them on the issue of expectation. For example you might have a client or patient say… "When my mother does X, Y, or Z, it makes me feel angry and stresses me out." The fact is, this person's expectation of his or her mother may be unrealistic in relationship to what the mother is capable of providing. The answer is not in changing the mother's actions or behavior (since neither the client nor you have any control over the mother) but rather in awakening the client or patient to the idea that their expectation of the other person is what needs to be reframed.

One method that I use in addressing expectation is that the client or patient needs to take back "the remote control of their life" from others. I instill as both waking hypnotic suggestion in the pre-talk, and as post hypnotic suggestion, the idea that no one can push their buttons unless they willingly give the remote control of their life over to another person. Expectation is one of the ways through which we give that control away. I have them imagine the remote control in their possession, and suggest that any time they feel that they are giving up that control, they will immediately take the remote control back. Sometimes I will actually give them an object that will act as their remote (The object can be virtually anything, even something as simple as a small stone or an eraser.). They can easily carry the object with them thereby creating a trigger mechanism to reinforce my suggestions to them. In addition, you can suggest erasing expectation. If they are visual, simply have them imagine the word "expectation" on the blackboard of their mind and then have them erase the word. By accepting that expectation leads to stress, and by erasing that expectation, you can help the client or patient to significantly reduce their levels of stress.

To some extent we all want the world to fit our individual standards. It is human nature to think that other drivers go too fast, or too slow, when obviously we are great drivers. It is human nature to think that others should share our brilliant views on child rearing, politics, and society. The fact is that others often do not share our views and to expect that is unrealistic. When we rid our clients or patients of expectation regarding others, and help them to take back "The Remote Control of Their Lives", we give them a powerful tool in the battle over stress.

PERCEPTION

If the person is properly prepared during the pre-talk, the hypnotherapy session is a cakewalk. You will be able to lock into the person's subconscious mind what the person has already accepted as not only possible but likely. You have created expectation and supplied the demand. By doing this in a way that empowers the person, their ability to manage stress will grow stronger and stronger with every day. They will lead a happier life, and be a walking, talking testimonial to your skills.

CONDUCTING AN EFFECTIVE SEXUAL DYSFUNCTION SESSION

One of the most emotionally painful and discouraging problems that a person can have is the inability to enjoy sexual relations. It is exasperating to the affected individual and often destructive to that person's relationship with a spouse or significant other. Sexual dysfunction can be caused by physical pathology and/or by emotional or psychological causes. When working with people in the area of sexual dysfunction the most important thing to determine initially is where the person's problem or circumstance originates. Even if the problem is physical in nature hypnotherapy can still be a useful adjunct in helping the person attain a great sex life. If the person's problem is emotional in nature then hypnotherapy is often the quickest and most powerful route to a resolution.

When a new person comes to me with problems related to sexual performance (or enjoyment) the first question I ask the person is whether or not he or she has seen a physician or urologist. It is important to know if there is a physical pathology or diagnosis that may be causing the problem in whole or in part. If they have been to a physician or urologist and there is no pathology, then chances are even better that I can help them achieve a great sex life. If a physician has not examined the person, I recommend that they consult a physician and have a thorough exam. Knowing what to rule in or out is critically important in structuring the person's hypnotherapy sessions.

During the consultation there is vital information that you need to acquire. For example, with men, I will ask about his ability to have an erection. With both men and women it is important to know if the person is able to achieve orgasm. Knowing under what circumstances the person does or does not experience a problem(s) is also vital information in constructing the therapy. For example, if a man has difficulty achieving or maintaining an erection during intercourse but is able to do so when masturbating, that provides reason to conclude that performance anxiety of some type (in relation to a partner) might likely be the issue. Likewise, if a woman can achieve orgasm while masturbating but not with her partner, we can conclude that performance anxiety may be the problem.

One issue to keep in mind is that failure to perform sexually often results in embarrassment and stress. This embarrassment and the ensuing stress reinforce and compound the anxiety thereby exacerbating the situation. A downward spiral then commences. It is up to the hypnotherapist to reverse this downward spiral. Each therapeutic move forward must be aimed at increasing the person's confidence and peace of mind, and his or her ability to feel worthy of enjoying each moment of the sexual experience.

THE VALUE OF HYPNOTHERAPY

Hypnotherapy is a powerful tool that can help people to achieve goals, overcome fears, banish anxieties and stress, and lead a more fulfilling life. There is nothing more basic in humans than the instinct and desire for sex. Sexual desire is a normal and natural instinct. It is provided by nature to assure the continuation of the species. It provides both an intimate feeling of being cared for and loved, as well as great physical pleasure and stimulation. Barring any physical or health related problem, by nature, we are all predisposed to enjoy an active sex life. Often, however, societal pressures, or religious and cultural biases, can interfere with this natural and healthy desire. This is often either the result of intentional or unintentional programming. We might say, "waking hypnotic suggestion".

Sex can be one of the most intimate and rewarding experiences that a person can enjoy. It is both a primary enforcer and (in most instances) a healthy and natural drive. The instinct to enjoy sex is part of the natural human experience. Many men and women however never fully experience the joy of a fulfilling sex life. The numbers are surprising. In my practice I see many people each year who are unable to have the quality of sexual pleasure that they desperately want and deserve. This is truly unfortunate and often unnecessary.

Since sexual perceptions and drives are housed in the subconscious mind, it stands to reason that hypnotherapy can be the most powerful way to explore and reprogram a person's issues concerning sexual enjoyment and free them to enjoy a great sex life. Hypnotherapy can facilitate powerful positive change by reframing perceptions about sex and by overcoming fear, insecurity, and guilt sometimes programmed into that person by waking hypnotic suggestion. This allows the person to open up to a wonderful and exciting sexual experience.

ENJOY SEX ?

Sex is a wonderful experience. I'm not advocating that everyone should take on the sixties "free love" (sex) mentality. I'm simply stating that the indoctrination or negative waking hypnotic suggestion(s) that many people have received as children often prevents people from enjoying sex to the fullest as an adult. Every person is different, but in general the indoctrination one receives in youth directly impacts our ability to enjoy sex as we reach maturity. The hypnotherapist must de-hypnotize (remove old suggestion) and replace them with more positive suggestion(s). As stated, sex is a normal and natural desire. Unfortunately, as with many things, we human beings deny rather than accept our nature. Often as children we are indoctrinated with waking hypnotic suggestion(s) about sex. These "waking hypnotic suggestions" often conflict with our natural desires thereby causing internal conflict. For example, often parents (either wittingly or unwittingly) plant within their children the seed that… sex is dirty ("Nice girls don't do that". "Boys who want sex are pigs" and so on.). As adults most of us know rationally and logically that nice girls do like sex and that boys who desire sex are not pigs simply because they have sexual desires. Those old messages however continue to reside deep within the minds of many people. The reason for this is simple. It is the conscious mind alone that contains the rational and logical thought processes that know that "sex is okay." Logical and rational thought, however, does little to alter subconscious perception. The only way to facilitate changes at the subconscious level is to speak directly to the subconscious mind without interference from the conscious mind (hypnosis). No matter what our conscious mind tells us, it will not change the perceptions created for the child within. Hypnosis is the vehicle that enables us to do that.

PERFORMANCE ANXIETY

We live in a very sexualized society. The prime time TV ads of today would have been far to risqué for even late night TV only a few years ago. It is virtually impossible to go to a movie, look through a magazine, or watch a TV program without seeing either blatant sexual references or at least sexual innuendo. You would think that this would give people a source of permission to enjoy sex that would make them more sexually secure. In fact, just the opposite often occurs. Shows and movies can create an unrealistic image of sex that many people feel unequipped to live up to. This often is a factor in "Performance Anxiety."

The general perception seems to be that performance anxiety effects mostly men. Although there are probably a greater number of men visibly affected by performance anxiety my finding has been that the numbers are not so far apart between men and women. It is simply more noticeable with men. Performance anxiety can make it difficult or impossible for a man to attain an erection thereby preventing lovemaking. Women obviously do not have this specific problem. The problem still exists however to the extent that a woman may not achieve the level of enjoyment from sex that she would like to, or perhaps she may be unable to achieve orgasm. These conditions can be disheartening and disruptive to self-esteem and destructive to the person's relationships with spouse or partner.

IN THE MOMENT

Remember, when a person experiences sexual dysfunction first you should find out if any physical pathology exists. Again, this is a job for a physician or a good urologist. If there is no pathology we can then look to other sources. As a practical point, in my practice I find that by far, performance anxiety is the most common reason preventing people from "experiencing the moment" and enjoying sex to the fullest. Staying in the moment is vital to fully enjoying sex. If the person wastes time worrying about what he or she did or didn't do a moment ago, or about what will be happening within the next few moments, the experience and joy of the moment will be missed. These thoughts are distractions. They can result in lovemaking becoming more of a job than a pleasure. Making love should in fact be carefree adult playtime, not an assignment. It is a time to share and enjoy, not a time to perform as if part of a circus act. Often performance anxiety causes people to take lovemaking far too seriously. The ability to "Enjoy the Moment" is vital to enjoying sex. Helping your client or patient to stay in the moment can be a big step forward in resolving his or her problem.

As an example, I have observed (by research and questioning… not voyeurism!) in both men and women anticipation of an orgasm may result in one of the following. It may prevent the orgasm, or it may reduce the intensity of the orgasm. In men it may sometimes have the opposite effect resulting in premature ejaculation thereby leaving both partners unfulfilled. Also, worry about whether a person will "live up to their partner's expectations" (or live up to some image of the perfect lover that they have from TV or movies) will take a person out of the moment. This can sabotage the opportunity for a wonderful sexual experience. As well, if he or she is thinking ahead to the orgasm or anticipating whether or not he or she will find reassurance, or rejection at the end of the lovemaking it will pull that person out of the moment thereby decreasing enjoyment. The moment is everything in lovemaking.

Before a hypnotherapy session I tell people that I want them to do more of nothing than they have ever done before and to simply relax and enjoy each moment of relaxation… like a massage for the mind. The fact is that with hypnosis, the less the person tries the better he or she does. To a great extent, this is true of sex as well. Often, the only thing needed to enable a person to have a better sex life is to provide them with the tools to stay in and enjoy the moment. Orgasm is only one part of sexual enjoyment. It is equally important that the person enjoy the moments of touch, of warmth, and of play. Each and every moment must be perceived as a precious entity unto itself. When the orgasm occurs, it too will be more fully experienced if the person is in the moment. After the person and his or her partner reach orgasm he or she can continue to enjoy the moments of sharing and touching that come after. Each moment only arrives once. If the person missed it because he or she was focusing on the moments past, or anticipating moments not yet arrived, he or she will miss the beauty of the here and now. You can help people to rediscover the wonders of sex. If you help your person to appreciate each moment as a separate and wonderful experience you can open the doors to a wonderful sex life for them.

HYPNOSIS AND PERFORMANCE ENHANCEMENT

BARRIERS TO SUCCESS

Most people create their own barriers to success. People are often unable to achieve levels of performance that accurately represent his or her true potential due to self imposed stumbling blocks. People, however, rarely see this as the reason. Instead they focus on external reasons for their lack of success. They place the blame on poor equipment, bad coaches or trainers, the weather, their shoes, or the direction of the wind. The fact is that most of the time the main reason(s) a person does not perform up to peak ability comes from within him or herself. More importantly, this is why he or she may fail to get the full enjoyment from an activity. Something that started out to be exciting and fun may ultimately become frustrating and annoying.

DISTRACTION

In my experience with helping people to increase performance I find the single most powerful reason that people fall short of their goal(s) is "distraction." In order to perform at maximum ability it is imperative that a person be "In The Moment." In fact, the approach to athletic performance enhancement is not so different from the general approach to helping people overcome some types of sexual dysfunction. The most frequent cause of failure or unhappiness with one's performance occurs when a person's focus is fragmented. This occurs most often because the person is dwelling in past or future events (For our purposes, past events represent anything that happened even a microsecond before, future events are anything that has not yet happened).

The vast majority of people that I see at my office for performance enhancement have one thing in common... When they are involved in an activity, they are either dwelling on what just happened (I should have done that differently. Why did I do that? Boy was that stupid, or Aren't I great, etc.), or they are anticipating what might happen (I hope I can do this, What if this happens, will this please my partner, coach, team, etc). Either of the two will take the person away from the most important time… the current moment. Not only has that person lost focus but he or she has also missed the beauty and the enjoyment of the moment. There is an old saying. "When you're up to your butt in alligators it's hard to remember that your prime objective was to drain the swamp". In my therapy practice I have seen first hand that this is true in sports, business, sex, art, music, and virtually everything that involves performance of any type. There is nothing more imperative to top performance than "being in the moment." Other distractions can include peer pressure, catering to a crowd of spectators (or worrying what they may think), comparing one's self to others, and probably the biggest of these distractions, worrying about winning or losing.

I believe it was Benjamin Franklin that said, "If you watch the pennies the dollars will take care of themselves." The same principle holds true with being in the moment. If you are totally in the moment, making the best of each and every moment, the minutes, hours, days and weeks, will take care of themselves. The most important ingredient to success is to maximize each and every moment. With total focus and ability concentrated within each moment, free from distraction of past or future events, a person will maximize his or her performance.

ENJOYMENT

For most people, the reason we get involved in an activity is because we like it… It's Fun! Too often, once involved in an activity, people lose sight of this. Winning or losing, or looking good to others takes precedent over simply enjoying the activity. I often wonder why a person continues to participate in an activity that drives them crazy. For example, why would a person play golf if the game gets them so mad that they wrap their gulf club around the nearest tree? That individual has lost total sight of why he or she took up the game in the first place.

The fact is that we usually function better when we are happy about what we are doing. After all, your heart will not be in something if it makes you angry and miserable. Performance is enhanced when a person enjoys an activity. It is not only a person's performance that is enhanced through the enjoyment, but his or her quality of life as well. If a person participates in an activity simply for the pleasure of doing so, he or she will gain greater benefit from that activity. It is not important what others think of your performance, who wins or who loses, or how you compare to others. Performance is maximized when a person simply takes pride in and enjoys what he or she is doing. My personal barometer of performance has nothing to do with anyone else on the planet. I simply do my best for the sole purpose of meeting my full potential. It has nothing to do with anyone else. And most importantly, I enjoy the things that I do.

FEAR

There are two fears that will impair performance. They are the fear of failure and the fear of success. Either can be equally detrimental to performance. As a practicing hypnotherapist and an instructor of hypnotherapy, I am well aware of the following phenomenon... What the mind expects to happen usually does happen. Part of my job as a hypnotherapist (when working with people for performance enhancement) is the function of being a mental coach and inspirational guide that can help the person re-define his or her perception of an activity. I become a facilitator of positive thought and affirmation. This is why many professional and Olympic athletes work with hypnotherapists and/or sports psychologists.

A preconceived fear or notion of failure will often lead to failure. As well, the mindset of, "I probably won't succeed" allows the person to give up before starting. It gives the lazy part of us license to take the easy way out. If the person accepts that they will fail then it lets him or her off the hook for trying.

Positive thought, on the other hand, usually brings positive results. What we believe will happen is more likely to happen. When a person visualizes success they are more likely to achieve success.

Fear of success can also inhibit performance. This can be especially true in a team or league setting. The chances of this becoming a factor are increased if the person is uncomfortable in the public eye, or uncomfortable being the center of attention. The perceived responsibility of "living up to" a particular level of performance in the future may cause that person to unconsciously sabotage their own performance. Again, the most important thing is perception. A good hypnotherapist can help a person to reframe for success by re-instilling focus on a personal level of simply opening up to his or her own potential for achievement, and to a fresh sense of enjoyment in the activity.

SELF TALK

Often we don't think about the power of words. In actuality, words are the most powerful thing in the world. Our entire perception and understanding of our world has been presented in the context of either the written, spoken, or signed word. We know how powerful words are when an adult speaks to a child. We are the giants. Our words are incredibly imposing to children. That is why children who are raised with words of encouragement are more often successful than children who are belittled and criticized. We know the power of words when one adult speaks to another. When someone says something complementary to you, you may feel "tickled" right down to your bones. If someone insults or belittles you, it can feel like a knot in your stomach. It can hurt emotionally and sometimes even manifest itself as physical discomfort. This being so, why then do we not recognize the importance of self-talk?

Positive thoughts bring positive results. Positive self-talk or affirmations help to form our self-image. Phrases like, "I can't," or "I'll never be as good as, (name)" predispose a person to failure. Conversely, positive self-talk can reframe us to achieve! The brain is like a computer. Whatever you program in, is what will come out. Doesn't it make more sense to program for success? Whatever your previous programming, you have the complete ability to reprogram for success. Positive self-talk is one important component in accomplishing that new programming.

PERFORMANCE

Anyone who desires to maximize his or her performance can. First, he or she must be willing to let go of the past (even that of a few seconds ago). There is nothing that anyone can do to change what has already occurred. Dwelling on past events accomplishes nothing. Next, one must not anticipate the future. The future is unborn. Anticipation only serves to draw you away from the moment at hand. Be "In The Moment." Enjoy what you are doing. Life is too precious to waste time in negative thought or in doing things that promote frustration. Speak to yourself in positive terms. By eliminating the negative and focusing on the positive anyone can meet their full potential. Anyone can maximize his or her performance with the power of his or her mind.

Chapter 12

Philosophy

SIMPLICITY IS THE KEY TO PEACE OF MIND

People will spend two, four, six, or eight years in college or trade school to learn a job skill. Most often, these same people spend virtually no time getting to know about themselves. This can be one source of great internal conflict. The fact that we in the field of hypnotherapy (and other alternative modalities) contribute to personal knowledge and growth is one of the reasons that we are continually growing in acceptance. For that matter, personal growth, understanding, and the enhancement of the quality of life, are the primary reasons that we exist.

It is important in moving ourselves (or our clients) in a positive direction to know not only what we want out of life, but also why we want it. Knowing why, gives us insight into our basic nature and will therefore help us to make better life decisions. The fact is, the decisions we make, as well as the tools that we give our clients to aid them in making positive decisions, more than any other single factor, governs the outcome of any individual's life. One way to see ourselves more clearly and thereby to make better life decisions is to simplify our approach to life. This is the philosophy that I live by and the one that I pass on to my clients and students.

Einstein once said "Reduce everything to it's simplest form but no further" (or something close to that). In life, we often seek complex answers to problems. If you seek complex answers, you will inadvertently complicate the problem as well. Seek simple answers to a problem, and the problem itself becomes simpler and less cumbersome. When someone tells me… "It's not that simple," it indicates immediately to me that he or she prefers to complicate the matter rather than to face the problem at hand. To solve a problem we must first own it. If we place (or allow our clients to place) the responsibility for life's problems on others, then it is not ours to solve. To resolve issues, we must first own our responsibility for them. Then, like peeling away the layers of an onion, we remove the excess until we get to the heart. Once at the heart of an issue, more often than not, the answer is very simple. I, therefore, help my clients to own their problem, face it, and find the simplest solution. It is important to make the distinction between simple and easy. The source of our problems in life is usually simple. That does not mean that resolving the issue will be easy. It takes owning and facing the dilemma and then taking the necessary steps to resolve it.

Some time ago, I had a client that had hidden a large sum of money. In fact, he hid it so well that he himself could not find it. In my first attempt to enhance his memory, I utilized regression therapy. I had him go back to that evening and relive his steps. He relived every moment in great detail… that is right up to the moment that he hid the money, and from right after that moment. He simply was not going to the particular moment that he hid the money. For about twenty minutes we continued with no results. Then an idea came to me. I emerged him from hypnosis. I asked him if he would like to do something "just for fun"… He agreed. I used a rapid induction to re-induce hypnosis. I knew, from our earlier discussion, that he liked fishing. In hypnosis, I took him out on a boat, on a wonderful fishing trip. When he was "reeling in a big one" I simply said to him… "This is great, and by the way, tell me where you hid the money so that I can get it for you." "It's under the cellar steps," he replied. The solution was simple. I just had to ask him where it was!

PERCEPTION

Much of life is how we perceive it. Or you might say that our perception often becomes our reality. When faced with a problem, most people will ask, "What else can I do, to solve this problem?" I have a suggestion. The next time you are faced with a problem, don't ask what additional measures you can take to solve the problem. That will only further complicate the problem. Instead, ask what I can let go of? Ask... What is really relevant to your (or your client's) goal? Then you will be able to focus on the truly meaningful aspects of the situation. View your actions as if you were peeling away the layers of an onion to get to the heart, because that is exactly what you need to do... Get to the heart of a problem. Once simplified, and recognized, any problem will be easier to resolve.

Our society seems to glorify complexity. This leads to stress and confusion. It is the simplification of our lives that will lead to a clear picture of our true needs and values and thereby lead to happiness. Happiness comes from within. How we (or our clients) view ourselves and view life in general will have greater impact on happiness or misery than any external force.

THE THREE LEVELS OF CONSCIOUSNESS AND HUMANITY

The past is gone and unchangeable. The future has yet to be revealed. The present is a means of developing our future. Great things are rarely accomplished in one explosive moment in our lives. Each deed that we do, whether positive or negative, constructive or destructive will, in the final analysis, represent who we are. Each small deed we do is a link in the chain of our existence on this plane. If our deeds are positive and generous, we will exist in a positive light. If the deeds we do are negative, we will exist as petty creatures. This is an evolutionary process and not something that happens by design or in an instant. By attempting to be great, a person will become infamous rather than famous. If you seek to do positive things and you have a generous heart, you will be viewed as a great person. This is due primarily to the motivation that drives these two very different types of minds. Adolph Hitler sought to be great. Although powerful (for a short time on the cosmic clock) his name will live in infamy as the personification of evil. Dr. Salk, on the other hand, sought to help humanity. He gave away his polio vaccine to benefit others. He will always be viewed as a great man. Their lives became products of the chain of deeds created by each man during his lifetime.

LEVELS OF HUMANITY

I have been involved in Shaolin Kung Fu for over 40 years. The meditation involved in that system is what led me into becoming a hypnotherapist. In the philosophy of the Kung Fu system that I teach, we believe that there are three levels of human consciousness and behavior. These levels are the spontaneous, the calculated, and the imposed. They each have unique characteristics that are described below.

Spontaneous – "Represents the highest form of consciousness because it dwells in the here and now. This mind can respond to life as it unfolds. It asks for nothing, harbors no ill for events of the past, and does not record or expect the repayment of debt. Because it expects nothing from others it is not disappointed. It does not seek to posses and is therefore never owned. From this non-possessiveness comes freedom, love. It demonstrates a receptive nature."

Calculated – "Represents the second level of consciousness. It is lower that the first because it requires manipulation. This mind attempts to steer events relative to its perception of right and wrong. It is focused on achieving the end that it thinks should happen. This results in a constant contention between what would be, and what this mind thinks should be. This mind's creative energy is confined by its need to direct others."

Imposed – "Represents the third and lowest level of consciousness because it requires force. It insists that all proceed in accordance with its plan. This methodology is both calculated and manipulative. As well, it addresses any opposition with punishment. This is rarely successful in the short term and never successful in the long term. A person of this mind becomes both jailer and prisoner. This mind is too focused on the control of events and people to experience life's wonders in the slightest way. It is a task-oriented mentality that sheds no light on what is really occurring."

FREEDOM

From where does freedom come? My philosophical belief is that it comes from adherence to the natural order. Manipulation and imposed force are a direct contradiction to this principle. Freedom comes from being one with the energy of the universe. It comes from being part of the process of living. This can only be achieved by first knowing ourselves. People will spend 2, 4, 6, 8 or more years in college learning a subject but often spend little or no time getting to know who they are or what, they themselves, truly think and feel. Some can go through their entire life and never have an original thought. A whole life can be spent vicariously living only second-hand thoughts and experiencing little. It is said that, knowing others is wisdom and knowing ourselves is enlightenment. It is also said in the philosophy that I follow that, mastering others requires force and that mastering ourselves requires strength.

THE PATH

True strength results in a giving and compassionate spirit. The need to exhibit force is a sure sign of insecurity. When we have truly overcome our own demons, we feel no need to control, condemn or punish others. If others attempt to oppress you, you can choose not to take part. You can choose to lead your life outside of the control of another. In Wing Chun Kung Fu we say... "If I do not resist you can not push." We all have the ability to choose our own path. No one can take that empowerment away from us. We only give it up by choice. Don't strive for greatness. Live a chain of positive deeds and you will find peace. If greatness comes from this, it is deserved.

Chapter 13

Meditation

WHAT IS MEDITATION

Meditation is a state of altered awareness that allows us to bypass previous programming and to open up to our higher self. It has been part of every society since the dawn of man. Virtually every religion has one form of meditation or another as part of its rituals. The fact is that almost everyone goes into a meditative state about a dozen times a week on average without even being aware of it. Have you ever stared out of a window and drifted away for a few moments losing complete track of time and surrounding activity? If you are a parent you know that kids do it all the time. When this happens the person has inadvertently gone into a meditative state. Meditation is not the act of thinking about something spiritual or creative, to the contrary it is the absence of conscious thought.

There are many different labels for meditation, as well as various approaches to achieving a meditative state. From various forms of Yogic meditation, or Shaolin meditation, to Transcendental Meditation, regardless of the vehicle the common denominator is pretty much the same. The ultimate goal is to open up to that intuitive, creative, and spiritual part of who we are. It is to access that higher part of our being.

Most everyone knows the word "meditation". Most people as well have some image in their mind about what meditation is. This perception is usually based on something they have seen on TV, or in the movies, like a Guru type individual sitting cross legged on a mountain. Few people however actually understand what meditation is.

ORIGINS

Meditation is as old as mankind. It is impossible for anyone to be certain where, when, and how, it came to be formalized. My studies lead me to believe that it evolved naturally. In many instances, people will spontaneously go into trance without trying to do so. From use as a natural escape mechanism (to avoid pain, heat or cold, or trauma), to something that may simply begin as daydreaming, trance is a naturally occurring phenomenon.

In ancient times those who were naturally more in tune with meditation or trance states found it to be a way by which he/she could open up to his/her inner wisdom. They found meditation a way to look at life through different eyes… or from another mountain or valley. Often these people became the spiritual leaders or wise men/women within the community. In turn, they would attract followers who could see the value in this process. The spiritual leader would then teach their followers these skills. Over the centuries various ways of teaching meditation skills became part and parcel to religious rituals.

Past civilizations most likely had an easier time meditating than people do in modern times. In our society we are trained from birth to be analytical and rational. How many times have you seen a small child who is playing and acting like a child be told by an adult to "act their age" (as if they are not), or to "grow up." This indoctrination serves only to inhibit the ability to meditate by stifling that creative and imaginative part of us. The childlike qualities within us are a vital component in achieving a meditative state.

MISCONCEPTIONS

Meditation is highly misunderstood. Meditation cannot be achieved through mechanisms like picturing a black dot on a black cloth, or by repeating affirmations about something that you would like to accomplish. To the contrary, meditation is the absence of all conscious thought. The deeper the meditation, the farther removed from conscious thought the person will be. Any attempt by a person to direct his/her meditation will actually deteriorate the state of trance. Meditation requires letting go of preconceived thought and opening up to nothingness. Only by letting go of all preconceptions can we accept what has not yet been discovered.

THE CONSCIOUS AND UNCONSCIOUS MIND

To understand meditation it is important to recognize how our minds work. Our minds function at two levels, the conscious mind and the subconscious mind. Our conscious mind is the analytical and/or task oriented part of us. It enables us to put a puzzle together, work out a mathematics problem, drive our car, etc. Your subconscious mind contains emotions, habits, perceptions, creativity, intuition, etc. The subconscious mind is also the little kid in us. It is the part of us that is not chained by the analytical rational adult part of us.

In western society we are taught from childhood to value the analytical and rational thought processes. Being imaginative or creative would not generally be held in the same esteem, as would someone being proficient at calculus. In much the same way as the lack of use of muscles will cause them to atrophy, the lack of use of the creative and intuitive part of who we are will cause spiritual atrophy.

Meditation is one of the best ways to exercise that all too often-neglected part of us. Be aware though that you cannot meditate with the conscious mind. You cannot "think about meditation" and have it happen. The opposite is necessary…you must let go of thought.

SOMNAMBULISM, HYPNOSIS, AND MEDITATION

Hypnosis and meditation have much in common. The major difference is simply that while hypnosis is "therapist or hypnotist driven," meditation is "free form." Both ideally will achieve a trance depth called somnambulism (or sometimes deeper). This depth is where we can leave the conscious thought process behind and are able to tap directly into our powerful subconscious mind.

Somnambulism requires bypassing what is called the critical faculty. The critical faculty, simplistically put, is the analytical and rational part of the conscious mind. When critical faculty bypass is achieved the result is somnambulism (or sometimes an even deeper trance-state). Conversely, critical faculty bypass requires absence of the conscious thought process. It is important to understand that any conscious thought would deteriorate the trance-state and bring the person out of somnambulism. For this reason a person "CANNOT" effectively facilitate suggestion or implement affirmation(s) while in trance since doing so would require conscious thought.

To achieve a true meditative state, or to maximize the therapeutic effects of hypnosis/hypnotherapy, the somnambulistic state of trance (or deeper) is necessary. This is difficult for many people to achieve simply because we are generally taught in western culture that the harder we try, the better we will do. In fact, with both meditation and hypnosis the opposite is true. The less we try, the better we do. By doing absolutely nothing we accomplish the best results. Achieving through not striving is a difficult concept for many people in modern western society to adjust to.

As well, I would suggest to you that the term "self-hypnosis" is a misnomer. Many people confuse the term self-hypnosis with both meditation and/or affirmations. The fact is that you cannot achieve a meditative or a hypnotic state and then make suggestions to yourself. As I have already stated, formulating suggestion requires conscious thought and conscious thought will bring a person out of somnambulistic (or deeper) trance. The only thing that could be accurately equated to self-hypnosis is if a person were to meditate (self induce trance) while playing a tape of predetermined, pre-recorded suggestions, or affirmations. Simply relaxing and repeating suggestions to yourself, is affirmation not meditation and not self-hypnosis. Allowing self-generated trance with no formalized structure is meditation (and not self-hypnosis).

Hypnosis and/or hypnotherapy allows for the hypnotist or hypnotherapist to help the subject/client/patient to achieve a somnambulistic (or deeper) state of trance. The hypnotist/hypnotherapist will then introduce suggestion based on what the subject/client/patient has indicated his/her goals to be. The work of formulating the suggestion is left to the hypnotist/hypnotherapist freeing the client/patient to simply do nothing except enjoy the wonderful feeling of trance.

True meditation is non-directive. The person allows trance state and then allows the subconscious mind to go wherever it needs to go for healing, development, or wisdom. (Note: Knowledge is accumulated by the conscious mind. Wisdom is collected by the subconscious mind) Although it is possible to "pre-imprint" where you would prefer to go within your meditation, there can be no conscious effort on the part of the participant to direct where the meditation will actually go. Analogous to this would be those cases where people (like myself) are able to wake up in the morning at a predetermined time without the use of an alarm clock. Before going to sleep I visualize what time I want to wake up in the morning. Then I give it no more thought. I simply go to sleep. In the morning I wake up within minutes of that time. Obviously laying in bed all night telling myself what time I want to awake would not work. The same is true with meditation. You can visualize where you want to go in your meditation before beginning, but once you begin, you must trust that your subconscious mind will take you where you need to be. Any attempt to control the process will bring the process to a screeching halt. In fact, one thing that will prevent meditation is actively "trying" to meditate.

COMPARING ANCIENT AND MODERN METHODS

By comparing ancient and modern methods of inducing trance we can get a more realistic picture of what meditation really is. As a practicing hypnotherapist and an instructor of hypnotherapy the similarities between ancient and modern trance inducing techniques are abundantly evident. For example: In ancient times people might stare at a candle until they ultimately went into trance. Today, in hypnotherapy, we would call that a fixation induction. This is where people go into hypnosis by staring at an object or a light, etc. In ancient times people would be induced into meditative trance by a technique called clacking (people hitting sticks together in rhythm to create a droning noise) or by chanting. This is similar to a hypnotic confusion induction where the person's conscious mind is overloaded with stimuli causing the conscious mind to escape or step aside. In ancient times focusing on the breath and relaxing more with each breath directly correlates to progressive relaxation induction (for many years the most common method of inducing hypnosis). These are just a few examples of how past methods of meditation are quite similar to current methods used in hypnosis/hypnotherapy. The state of mind that is sought is the same in both instances.

Today technology expands to an even greater degree the methods by which we can achieve meditative trance states. Some people have found success using biofeedback techniques. I have found devices like the "Photosonix" or "Mind Machine" to be valuable in helping people through the initial stages of learning to meditate. [Note: info available at www.photosonix .com] Much of this equipment is the result of biofeedback research. It combines frequencies of sound with patterns of light that often help to facilitate trance state. The devices include a number of programs that you can select from based on what you are looking to accomplish (opening up to creativity, meditation, etc.). These programs may vary depending on manufacturer. I have been using one in my office since about 1997 (with select clients and patients) and have had good results. Many of the people that have used them at my office have since purchased their own units.

Likewise, there are many electronic devices that are no more than toys. Be sure to look over the data and if possible talk to people who have used any device that you are considering. These electronic devices are certainly not necessary for meditation however they can be helpful… especially for those who have a particularly hard time letting go of the conscious mind. Be sure to read all product warnings before using such devices. For example, those with seizure disorders (epilepsy, etc.) should not use certain devices for the same reasons that they should avoid strobe lighting. If you have any doubts as to whether one of these devices might be right for you, check with your physician before using or purchasing one.

TIPS FOR MEDITATION

One of the most common problems people relay to me when they come to study meditation is this. They'll say, "Dr. Holder, when I try to meditate I start thinking about lots of different things and I can't get them out of my mind. I try to get them out but I just can't."
The problem is not the thoughts but the fact that the person is trying to get rid of them. By doing so the person shoots himself/herself in the meditative foot. Allow all images to process naturally. These images or sensations may be coherent or they may make absolutely no sense at all (in a cognitive way). It makes no difference. If you are non-directive they will pass/process naturally as your trance ability improves.

Often people are under the misconception that a special body position is necessary for meditation. This is not true. People who have spent years meditating in a lotus or some other exotic position are comfortable doing so. If the average person were to attempt to sit like that he/she would probably spend the entire time thinking about the pain in his/her legs and hips while wondering if he/she will ever walk again when he/she tries to get up. You should simply find a place and a position in which you feel comfortable, safe, and secure for your meditations.

Once comfortable, you can allow each breath you exhale to carry you deeper into a peaceful relaxation. Open up to the child within you. There is no right or wrong sensation(s). Your meditation will be unique to you. Logic and rational thought have no place in this special world. If you feel compelled to follow the same rational thought processes that you follow throughout the routines of the day you will be anchored in that and will be unable to achieve meditation. To experience original thought it is important to leave the world of physics and societal training behind for a short while. Only then will you experience the benefits that meditation can bring.

In short, by doing nothing all can come to you. Attempting meditation with an agenda will simply provide you with a trip to where you have already been. Expecting nothing will bring you whatever you need. Directing nothing will take you to places you've never before experienced.

HOW TO UNLOCK THE CREATIVE POWER WITHIN

Trance state is the only path to true original thought. After all, a hypnotic induction is nothing more that a tool used to get the conscious mind to step aside so that we can speak directly to the subconscious mind. I believe that all of the great artists, musicians, inventors, and writers, throughout history spent a significant portion of their lives in trance. Perhaps the biggest difference between the average person and a great painter, musician, or inventor, lays simply in the fact that the artist, by nature, had the characteristic ability of being able to frequently, and spontaneously go into trance state (in most cases probably not knowing they were even doing so).

Trance state allows the creative talents, intuitive ability, imaginative qualities, perceptual flexibility, and the emotionally honest, part of who we are, to freely explore ideas that were never seen in the mind's eye before. It allows us to bypass all of the, "It couldn't work," "How could that be," or "That doesn't make sense" hang-ups and to simply enjoy the creative process.

Meditation, hypnosis, or for that matter any spontaneous or induced trance state allows the subconscious mind to be free from the conscious restraints which are present in the conscious waking state. The more you exercise a muscle the stronger it becomes. Likewise, the more you exercise your inner creative child, through vehicles like meditation, and hypnosis, the more powerful your intuitive and creative powers become. Conscious thought can only take you over paths you have already traveled. New and original thought can only be achieved by letting go of the conscious mind and allowing the trance state to free the wonderful creative powers within you.

Chapter 14

Practical Issues and Practice Management

In recent years there has been an increased awareness of alternative health modalities and an increased interest in holistic health. These alternative methods of wellness are nothing new. What is new is the mainstream acceptance that has been developing. People have begun to realize the wonderful benefits that alternative wellness modalities can provide. This is especially true when they are used in conjunction with modern medical methods.

I have been involved in alternative health methods for decades. It started with my involvement in classical Shaolin Kung Fu. Acupressure, acupuncture, shiatsu, herbology, meditation, and the like have been part and parcel to traditional Shaolin training for over three thousand years. My background and connection to these ancient arts provided me with the great opportunity to study many alternative health methods long before they were trendy or accepted. My studies in the sixties and seventies, in meditation, in fact, are what led me into my profession as a hypnotherapist. Even though these wonderful methods for maintaining health have existed for a very long time, only now are they beginning to gain widespread acceptance in the U.S. under the label of holistic health. Western medicine, as well as the general public now realize what many of us who have been involved in alternative wellness have long advocated… It is better, cheaper, and easier to live healthy and to stay well, than it is to cure the problem after your health has declined. To date, while holistic practitioners have advocated healthy alternatives, western medicine, and the pharmaceutical companies, for the most part, have continued to focus on curative medicine. That is to say striving to recover wellness after it has been lost.

Exact Science

The complaint that I have heard most often about holistic modalities is that they are not an exact science. For example, a western M.D. commented to me that he doesn't know how acupuncture works, so he doesn't believe in its use. I have also heard, there is not enough scientific data about herbs to utilize them when in fact they have been successfully used for thousands of years. Personally I believe, if they prove helpful to those using them, and if there is no body of evidence of harm from their use, there is no reason not to use them. This is not to say that care should not be taken… it certainly should be. Experienced holistic practitioners or medical practitioners who have made a career of these studies should be consulted if you plan to use herbs and natural remedies. This is for two reasons. First, for best results natural remedies must be used in proper amounts just as with pharmaceuticals. This is simply a matter of common sense. Secondly, even though side effects are far less common with natural remedies, one can waste a lot of money purchasing homeopathic/herbal supplements that simply may not be right for them. It is always best to seek the advice of a skilled professional. As well, herbs are the forerunner of modern day pharmaceuticals and used improperly can have adverse effects. Herbs are not jellybeans or snack food.

To those who view holistic wellness as an inexact science be aware that western medicine, as well, is not an exact science. How many times have you seen someone go to more than one M.D. and gotten a totally different opinion from each as to what was wrong. How many times have you known a physician to change a patient's medication two, three, four, or more times until that physician found the one that he or she felt would work. How often has someone had surgery and found the cure to be worse than the original ailment. This certainly doesn't sound like an exact science. The fact is that neither holistic health methods nor modern western medicine are exact sciences. The best results are achieved with a balance of both modern and complementary approaches conducted by well-trained, knowledgeable professionals in the field.

Holistic Health

The goal of holistic health is to promote health and wellness. The idea is to create both a physical and mental state of balance that better equips the body to ward off illness. If illness should occur, conservative methods, and natural remedies would be the first line of defense rather than chemical medications that could have harsher side effects or be toxic to the body. I believe that most people would find this concept reasonable. On the other hand, if my appendix is about to burst, please get me a good surgeon. An intelligent balance of homeopathic, herbal and modern techniques can provide the best benefit.

WESTERN MEDICINE AND HOLISTIC WELLNESS

In recent years many medical practitioners are beginning to offer holistic services...some having very little experience in the field of homeopathy. This is no different than if an acupuncturist decided to take out someone's tonsils without the proper medical training. If you want to know why western medicine is now singing a different tune about holistic wellness I think I have the answer... follow the money. Although there are many sincere medical practitioners who truly see the benefits of homeopathy for their patients, and bring in qualified people to fill those positions, there are also those who simply see a golden goose. Maybe there are some, to one extent or another, fall into both categories. Today we as a country spend billions each year on complementary services, herb, and supplements. This is certainly an enticement for people of all backgrounds to enter the profession.

For those of us that are in the holistic professions, there has been an up and a down side to the new interest in holistic care. The down side is simple. Years ago, medical doctors, for the most part, scoffed at holistic health methods. They condemned everything from chiropractic to acupuncture as hooey. Now that the public is accepting and benefiting from these methods many medical professionals not only want a piece of the pie, they want complete control. The fact is a western physician's training is far different than that of a holistic practitioner. Holistic practitioners are primarily concerned with how to maintain health. Western physicians, for the most, are trained in how to cure disease. The approaches are significantly different.

A couple of years ago, the AMA, pharmaceutical companies, and other medical groups, lobbied to make vitamins and natural supplements available by prescription only. It doesn't take a rocket scientist to figure out why. These groups cannot patent natural substances (herbs, and other such supplements), like they can with synthesized medications, so they simply sought another way to get into your pocket. Making vitamins etc. available by prescription only was a way to accomplish this. The fact is we don't hear of people dying from ginseng or daily vitamins.

I know people who are highly skilled in acupuncture who had been practicing either in the US of overseas for decades. They can no longer practice in many states in the

USA. Many states require that you either be an M.D. or be working under the direction of an M.D. to perform acupuncture because of the insertion of needles. Although these skilled professionals are prohibited from practicing it is often easy for an M.D. to take a two-week quickie course and add acupuncture to his or her list of services (scary isn't it!).

Another example is apparent in my field of hypnotherapy. Myself, as well as many of my colleagues, have thousands of hours of hypnotherapy training. Many of us continue study on an ongoing basis. There are those in the psychiatric field would like to see hypnotherapy come under their umbrella even though their own hypnotherapy training is intensely lacking. The reason… with the growing acceptance of hypnotherapy (thanks to those of us who have persevered through the lean years), they smell a cash cow. Hypnotherapy is a totally different and unique field. Contrary to popular belief, in hypnotherapy, the methods and training are far different than those studied in psychiatry or psychology. Those of you in the hypnotherapy profession are keenly aware of that.

The Up Side

The up side is that we in the holistic professions are now able to help far more people than in the past because of the growing interest in and acceptance of alternative care. Can we help everybody? No of course we can't. Do we have a one hundred percent track record of success? Of course not. But then neither do western medical practitioners. They are both inexact sciences.

I am not putting down western medicine by a long shot. There are many caring and competent doctors, nurses, and technicians in the medical profession. As well, I am not implying that all holistic practitioners are what they should be. We have our share of misfits too. Just as in all professions, you have good, bad, and varying degrees in between. Further, I have no objection to the licensing of holistic health professions. In fact, I support it. Holistic practitioners of all types, however, should be licensed as the separate and unique professions they are. The important consideration is to give the public options and "alternatives" in achieving greater health and peace of mind.

Balance Of Conventional And Alternative

With dedicated practitioners of both alternative care and western medicine, who truly desire to help people to a healthier life, all will benefit. It is my opinion that it is best to specialize in your chosen field (hypnotherapy, NLP, acupuncture, herbology, etc.) rather than trying to be a "Jack of all trades" and therefore a master of none. For the integrity and reputation of our profession, complementary practitioners should never make outrageous claims (holistic modalities can be very beneficial but they are not magic). Those who make unfounded claims give ammunition to those who would like to see us out of business. At the same time make sure that your client's expectations are realistic.

You can help those who come to you to vastly improve the quality of their lives. Just as we in the holistic fields are not medical doctors, medical professionals are not generally schooled in holistic wellness. We are unique. It is my hope in the years to come to see holistic practitioners and medical professionals working more closely together for the benefit of those we serve.

PRACTICAL MATTERS: TIPS FOR DEVELOPING A SUCCESSFUL PRACTICE

Each year I see hypnotherapists and holistic practitioners go in and out of business. Often they have the skills of their profession (hypnosis etc.), but no skills in running a practice. This is one of the reasons that I require an internship from my hypnotherapy students. They not only experience first hand the therapeutic aspect of running a successful practice, but they also experience the daily running of an office. It takes more than the ability to induce hypnosis to run a successful hypnotherapy office.

FIRST IMPRESSIONS

In order to build a successful practice, people must have faith in your abilities. This starts with the first contact. That contact may be by way of written literature, advertisement, phone call, or by a personal meeting. In any event, this contact will in great part determine whether or not the person will come to you. The following are some simple suggestions to help you make the best of that contact.
Literature:

Make sure that your cards, flyers, and mailers have a professional touch. Always include a photo so that the people reading it will see "the person" that you are. Make your literature educational and informative. Introducing yourself in your literature is fine, but keep most of your flyer centered on educating the reader about your profession, and most importantly telling them "What It Can Do For Them!" This gives the person a sense of security and a feeling that you know what you are talking about.

I recommend that you always have a separate business phone line. This holds true even if your office is in your home. Always answer the phone in a polite and professional manner. We answer our phones, "Master's Center, can I help you." Never have children or those with a poor telephone demeanor answer your business phone. It will reflect poorly on your level of professionalism. Make sure that the person answering the phone (if it is not you) is trained in what to say and what not to say. Be sure to always get the caller's name, phone number (with area code) and address (with zip code) before giving out any information. This gives you a way to follow up in the event that one of you must end the call abruptly. As well, always follow up your phone contact with a mailing.

THE PERSONAL MEETING

When first meeting a potential client it is important to have a professional appearance and a friendly yet professional demeanor. What I am about to say has in the past ticked some people off, but "I call-em like I see-em!" PEOPLE DO JUDGE A BOOK BY ITS COVER. If you want a successful practice you must accept this as fact. Dress professionally (no white coats please). Men should wear dress pants and a dress shirt. A tie isn't necessary but will work. Lose the Jeans and trendy shirts. Hair to the middle of your back (men) will turn off many clients (especially the professional who can more easily afford your services). Also be clean-shaven, or if bearded, keep your beard or mustache trimmed. Some "would-be-therapists" may think it looks earthy to have long hair and a scraggily beard, but to the average potential client it looks unprofessional. Jeans and long hair may look good for someone working in a biker shop, but you probably won't have a successful practice if you present that image.

Women should dress professionally. Avoid trendy hairstyles and cloths (and lose the pierced nose ring). Also avoid 60's love and peace attire, casual sandals and heavy make-up. If you want to be treated like a respected professional, then you must present yourself as one.

It may offend some people that we are judged by their appearance, but like it or not that's reality. If you want to make a statement with trendy cloths, nose and tongue piercing, or hair to the waist (men), you can do that... it's your privilege. You may however need to find another profession. It is all a matter of priorities.

YOUR OFFICE

Your office should be neat, non-clinical, and attractive. Make your therapy room friendly and inviting. For example, I keep all of my diplomas, etc. on my business office wall. There are none in my therapy room. My therapy room is simple and homey. Have your appointment cards professionally done. Nothing looks tackier than writing your client's follow-up visits on a piece of scrap paper. Have standard client forms for them to fill out when they come to see you. This helps you to stay organized and makes for a more professional appearance. These little touches go a long way. Don't overbook! People get antsy when they have to wait for an extended period of time. That will get you off on the wrong foot. Just think about how you feel when you have a 10:00 appointment with your family physician and he takes you in at 11:00.

BOTTOM LINE

Most people don't lose their practices because they don't know hypnotherapy (or whatever the profession may be). They lose them because they don't present themselves or their profession in a positive and professional way. Hypnotherapy and alternative wellness methodologies are emerging growth professions. If you are competent in your field, and present yourself as a professional, you can build a wonderful and lucrative practice.

THERAPY TAKES TIME

Hypnotherapy is no different than any other therapy in that it requires a structured approach. As well, hypnotherapy has no magical powers to instantly transform people's lives. Therapy is not an event it is a process where methodically the therapist can help to move a person from a place of negativity and/or stagnation, to a life of positive thought and forward momentum.

Prior to the fifties and sixties when people went to a hypnotist (the word hypnotherapist was rarely used at that time), they expected to go for multiple sessions. At some point in time hypnotists began to promote the idea that in one easy session he or she could resolve all of the subject's woes. This was probably great for the quick-buck conmen but it did not do much toward showing hypnotists or hypnotherapists to be therapeutic professionals.

Even today I see hypnotherapists advertising that one session can fix just about anything from weight loss to removing hemorrhoids. Think about it… In no other profession do its members make such overstated claims. No one, not your physician, chiropractor, dentist, or for that matter your car mechanic, can in all honesty say that one visit will do the trick. Why then do some in the profession of hypnotherapy think that they have this supernatural ability? That attitude is in no one's best interest. It makes the profession of hypnotherapy look shabby. It makes the person advertising one-session-magic look like a charlatan, and it obstructs the path to professional, quality therapy for the client/patient.

The fact is that many people will respond well in one session for the short term. The problem is that long-term success is better facilitated with a program of therapy. Some years ago I tracked the results of clients/patients who had come for smoke cessation and weight loss. Some of them did only one session. Others completed a three-session program. In brief the results were as follows. The vast majority of people who came in for the sessions, in the short term, accomplished their goal. For example most of the smokers initially stopped smoking. After almost two years, however, the clients/patients that completed the three-session program had far higher incidents of remaining a non-smoker or keeping the weight off than did the one-session group.

This becomes even more important when we are dealing with more complex issues. The added impact of multiple sessions, carefully constructed to address not only the superficial symptoms but also the underlying mechanism, will enable the client/patient to experience not only better but also more durable results. This concept is what separates a quick fix from true and professional therapy.

If a practitioner wants to be perceived as a professional it is important that he or she perform in a professional way. This is also good business. When people are successful (over the long haul) it reflects positively on both the practitioner and on the profession of hypnotherapy as a whole. Therapist's actions, level of professionalism, and the results that he or she gets over the years will determine if he or she makes it in their practice or is a flash in the pan.

Referrals should make up a significant part of a

therapist's practice after the first couple of years. The only way to develop referrals is by giving people what they are paying for. Having past clients/patients say about you, "Well it worked at first but I went back to smoking in a few weeks," is not going to help you build a practice. Having them say, Boy was that guy (or gal) great. I haven't had a cigarette in two years," are more valuable than any paid advertising in assuring success.

Chapter 15

ADVERTISING

Advertising can be expensive. You can bet that as soon as you open your practice, advertisers will come out of the woodwork, each swearing that their publication, or station, will bring you more business that you could ever handle. The fact of the matter is that most advertising costs a lot while bringing in little. That is why you must use your advertising dollars wisely.

Advertising a professional practice is primarily about name recognition. In my experience the most important ad to have is Yellow Pages. This doesn't mean that you need a half-page display ad. I have found that a small display ad works just fine. I like to include a photo of myself within the ad. The purpose of the photo is to begin establishing a sense of familiarity at the earliest possible time. Prospective clients or patients will generally call the person that they feel most comfortable with. At this stage, your ad is the only thing they have to go by. As well, I find it helpful to place yellow pages "one-liners" in other areas of the yellow pages that relate to a hypnotherapy practice (e.g.: Smoke Cessation, Weight Loss, Stress Management, etc.), with a notice to "refer to our ad on page 123."

FREE IS GOOD

You can get lots of free advertising by running programs through local adult education programs and for civic, fraternal, and religious organizations. They send out flyers and schedules about events and classes they are hosting to their mailing list(s) and guess what... Your name should be in them. Remember, the key is name recognition.

You will probably not set the world on fire with any one specific ad, but you need to be in public view consistently. Many small ads will generally do more in generating business than one big ad. People don't always pick up the phone the first time they see an ad… Do You?

Here is the real scenario. A person picks up a local magazine and sees your ad. They say to themselves, "that looks interesting," they put the magazine down and go shopping. The next week that same person receives an announcement from the local school system about upcoming adult education classes. Your name is in it. The person reads the pamphlet, throws it in the trash, and lies down on the couch. A month or two later that same person decides that he or she just has to lose weight. They look in the phonebook under either weight loss, or hypnotherapy. Your name is there. Not only is it there, there is something familiar about your name. They pick up the phone and call you. That is how advertising can work for you.

Last but not least. To most people, if you do not have an ad in the Yellow Pages, you are not a "real business." Big or small it is important that you have a Yellow Pages ad (I stay away from the copy-cat yellow pages books and stick to the main phone company book). The other thing is, you must answer the phone. I tell my students that, "He (or she) who answers the phone will get the work. Often time people do not want to leave personal information on a tape. They want to talk to someone who can explain the process of hypnotherapy.

THE "PRE" PRE-TALK BROCHURE
(Start prepping the client/patient early)

I love my work. No matter how much you love what you do you must, of course, be able to make a living at it if you want to do it as a full time profession. One way I have found to maximize my efforts is through a multipurpose brochure. With a brochure like the one I will describe, you can help both your clients and yourself. You can reduce your workload and decrease your chance of "Burn Out" from wearing the many hats that self employed professionals must often wear...(therapist, publicist, spokesperson, ad exec, etc.). You can focus more energy on your work. As well, your clients will be better prepared and more receptive to therapy. Your brochure, sent in advance, can begin the preparation process before a client ever visits your office

DESIGNING A GREAT BROCHURE

The brochure I use is in a constant state of evolution. It keeps getting better as time goes by (with regular subtle changes). The basic concept I use is simple... Allow your brochure to accomplish these three functions:

1. Advertisement:

Let prospective clients see who you are and what you do. The cover should include catch phrases and power words that will captivate their interest. Keep it simple. Large print that can be read from a distance is best for the cover page. The cover should only include enough information to peak the person's curiosity. The purpose of the cover is to get them to open the brochure and read what is inside. A photo of yourself is great to include in the brochure too. With a photo, prospective clients are immediately associating a face with the information provided within, or with the voice on the telephone. You are now a visible, tangible person instead of a commodity, business, or thing.

2. Educate and dispel fears:

After all these years, it is still surprising to me how many misconceptions there still are about hypnosis. Many people don't pick up the phone and call for information simply because they already believe their skewed impressions about hypnosis are true and accurate (often resulting in unfounded fears). I'm sure you all know what I am talking about. In my office, on the street, in my workshops, with friends, and in dealing with people in other areas of business, I am constantly reminded of the inaccurate perceptions people have of hypnosis. These inaccurate perceptions often prevent potential clients from even making the initial contact call. As a matter of curiosity, however, they will pick up and read a well written, informative, and eye-catching brochure.

This brochure can and should be friendly, it should calm fears, educate, and inspire. I include primarily basic information on how hypnosis works and an abundance of information designed specifically to dispel fears. As well, I provide some information about myself and about my professional philosophy. This creates a rapport with the prospective client even before we talk on the phone or meet face to face. To some extent, the prospective client already feels he or she knows me, and is comfortable with me... even at this early stage. This is a tremendous benefit in session and will increase your success rate.

3. Provide a "Pre" Pre-Talk (So that in effect, your office pre-talk reinforces the written pre-talk).

If compounding and reinforcement are important in establishing durable suggestions in hypnosis, why should we assume this principle to be less important when acquiring new clients? Your brochure should act as your "pre" pre-talk. When you do this, your office pre-talk will reinforce, and compound the ideas and suggestions that your client has already read in your brochure. As well, printed material is very powerful. For example, look at how many people believe the outrageous stories in many tabloids (e.g. woman gives birth to child who is half giraffe.). If people will believe ridiculous tabloid information, just because it is in a paper, it is logical to assume that they are even more likely to believe the honest, rational, intelligent, and factual material that is presented in a professional manner within your brochure. By using your brochure as a "Pre" Pre-Talk new clients are already prepared for hypnosis, to a significant degree, when they come into your office for the first time... Even prior to your one-on-one intake and pre-talk.

ADDITIONAL POINTERS

Our profession is now emerging from the shadowy image (no thanks to Count Dracula and other negative movie impressions) that it once had. We are finally gaining public acceptance. I remember thirty, twenty, even ten years ago, many people thought that acupuncture and chiropractic were quackery. In the same way that acupuncture and chiropractic have emerged as wonderful and healthful tools, hypnosis is on the road to being accepted by the mainstream. We (hypnotherapists) owe it to our profession and to our colleagues to represent our profession with dignity. Your brochure should be designed with that in mind. Here are some ways that you can accomplish that:

1. Make your brochure factual and honest. Keep all promises/client expectations realistic. Making claims that hypnosis can remedy problems that it cannot, or that it can remedy problems that should be handled by another type of practitioner, will make you appear dishonest and a charlatan.

2. Stay away from circus theatrics or implications of mystic powers. These claims will put the image of our profession back 100 years.

3. Keep it simple. Use words that everyone can understand, not professional jargon. This will help give the reader a sense of comfort and confidence. This is not the time to show how smart you are, it is a time to help a potential client feel comfortable about approaching you.

HOW TO PUBLISH A GOOD BROCHURE INEXPENSIVELY

If you have a computer and a good publishing program you're set. I use Microsoft Publisher but there are many good programs that are similar. One advantage of generating your brochure on your PC is that you can modify and update it when you get new ideas for a better brochure. I use the three-fold brochure format/template in the program itself. The three fold brochures are easier to carry, place, mail and store. There are inexpensive plastic stands available, at any good office supply outlet, for displaying your brochures neatly and professionally.

The next step is to take a high quality printout of your brochure to a local copy center. These centers are generally cheaper than conventional printers because of the volume of work they do. The copies are of a satisfactory quality for brochures. For one thousand, two sided, pre-folded brochures, with a photo, I pay around $75.00. My return on this investment has been substantial.

If you have all the free time in the world, you may feel that you don't need a multipurpose brochure. You may feel that you have the time to wear the many hats often needed to run a practice. Then again, if you have all the time in the world, you probably are not working with too many clients and would therefore benefit greatly from such a marketing tool. If you are working with many clients, this might be a good way to economize your time.

Chapter 16

Sample Documents

The following documents are examples only and are not for use or reproduction.

Dear Client/Patient,

Please take a 5 minute transitioning period and relax in our waiting area before leaving.

Re-adjusting gradually to the sights and sounds outside of this office will be helpful to you in achieving your goal.

Thanks!

Client/Patient Profile Sheet (P. 1)

Client/Patient Profile
Page #1
Business Name

Date: ____________

Last Name: ______________________ First Name: ______________________ MI: ________

Address: ____ Apt./Suite ______________

City: ___________________________ State: ______________ Zip: ______________________

Day Phone: (____)__________ Eve. Phone: (____)__________ Fax: (____)__________

Email: ______________________ Date of Birth: ________ SS # (required): ______________

Occupation: ____

Credit Card (required for accepting check) Visa / Mastercard / Am Express: ______________

Spouse: _______________ Parent or closest relative: _______________ Phone: __________

Children: 1. ________________________________ Age __________
2. ________________________________ Age __________
3. ________________________________ Age __________
4. ________________________________ Age __________

Reason for Visit: ____

How did you hear about us:

____

Physician: ______________________________
Physician's Address: ____
City: ______________________ State: ______________ Zip: ______________________
Phone: (____)______________

Please check below the areas that you think you could most benefit from. Your open and honest responses will best help us to help you in achieving your goals.

- ☐ Smoke Cessation
- ☐ Fears and Phobias
- ☐ Weight Loss
- ☐ Anxiety
- ☐ Memory Enhancement
- ☐ Improving Relationships
- ☐ Regression Therapy
- ☐ Meditation
- ☐ Addictions
- ☐ Stress Management
- ☐ Pain Control
- ☐ Performance Enhancement
- ☐ Sexual Problems
- ☐ Self Esteem/Appreciation
- ☐ Breaking Negative Habits
- ☐ Bed Wetting
- ☐ Forensic Hypnosis
- ☐ Goal Achievement (athletic)
- ☐ Goal Achievement (School Grades)
- ☐ Goal Achievement (General)
- ☐ Behavior Modification
- ☐ Development of Intuitive Powers
- ☐ Tapping into your inner creativity
- ☐ Hypno-Birthing
- ☐ Other (use space provided below)

Other: ____

____

Business Name
Offers, Non-Chemical, Non-Medical, Non-Invasive alternatives to promote health and wellness !

Client Profile Page #2
Session Prices

Hypnotherapy / Counseling ----- $175.00 per session and/or $350.00 for our 3 session Programs. First session includes intake & personal consultation. Three session programs are payable in full on the first visit to qualify for the discount. Discounts cannot be combined with any other offer. All payments for sessions booked are non-refundable and are not transferable (all sales are final). Three session program must be completed within 45 days of the initial visit or balance may be forfeited at the discretion of Business Name. Note: Prices are subject to change from time to time without prior notice.

Regarding Hypnotherapy: There are times when one hypnotherapy session can be effective in achieving your goal, but hypnosis is a tool, not a magic bullet. Its effectiveness is a combination of positive suggestion, and your determination to achieve your goal. With some people, multiple sessions may be required to achieve the desired effect. Business Name reserves the right to tape any sessions or consultations for our records. All client records/material are kept in confidence. Be aware that hypnosis, meditation, and counseling require your complete and willing participation to be effective. Unlike the movies, under hypnosis, you cannot be made to do anything that you do not truly desire to do, or anything that violates your moral, personal, or religious convictions. Positive and wonderful changes can happen if you truly desire them to. You are an active part of that process. After your session(s), please take 5 or 10 minutes to relax in our waiting area. This transitional period will be helpful to you.

Unfortunately, there are those who lack good manners and a respect for the time and schedules of others. We trust that this does not include you. For those who would be so inconsiderate, we adhere strictly to the following policy. Except for impassable weather conditions or extreme emergencies, cancellations or appointment changes must be made at least 24 business hours in advance. In signing this form you agree to pay for any missed appointments if this 24-hour notice is not given. Clients acknowledge that they can be held responsible to pay reasonable collection and attorney's fees incurred in the collection of outstanding balances. A significant amount of time (1 to 2 hours) is set aside specifically for you. Fifteen minutes or more late will be considered a missed appointment. It is normally impossible for me to fill a cancellation on short notice so...

PLEASE KEEP YOUR APPOINTMENT IN A TIMELY FASHION OR YOU WILL BE CHARGED FOR THE APPOINTMENT!

Clients/patients/students will be charged $25.00 for checks (or credit card charges) returned un-payable for any reason. He/She authorizes Business Name to bill his/her credit card (given on reverse side) for services & charges for checks returned. Payment is due when services are rendered. If you require a receipt you must request it when payment is made. We cannot provide receipts after that time. Should we make an exception for you there will be a $25.00 minimum charge for receipts or statements provided after the date of payment.

Information Disclosure/Liability Release/Waiver/Disclaimer

Dear Client,

We/I do not practice medicine. Hypnosis/Hypnotherapy is a unique and separate profession as are counseling and psychotherapy. Through the use of hypnosis/hypnotherapy, counseling, and related holistic methods we can help you to accomplish your goals. We/I do not prescribe drugs or related treatment. After consultation we/I can suggest alternatives, and provide services that may be utilized to enhance your well being, and help you accomplish your goal(s). **Note**: Those under the care of a physician should not ignore your doctor's advice for medical problems. Consult with your physician before making any changes in his/her prescribed treatment. Our philosophy is not intended to be a replacement. It is an additional method to help you accomplish your goal(s). Re: Holistic, alternative modalities: We/I believe in the ancient principle that the body's own energy in cooperation with proper healthful diet, and a positive mental attitude, can prevent and/or correct imbalance and allow the body to repair itself and the mind to rejuvenate itself (e.g. acupuncture, acupressure, meditation, hypnoses, etc.) These programs are also designed to contribute to developing a greater personal sense of well-being, happiness, and healthiness. It is the your option whether or not to exercise the suggestions. We offer guidance and assistance. The result of this can be a healthier, happier life.

For your added safety, disclose of all Pre-existing Medical/Health Conditions here (And do you have a family history of any of the following). Use a separate sheet if necessary): ☐ Heart Problems ☐Back or Neck problems ☐ Seizure Disorders (If yes explain). ________

Other: ____

I have read and understand the above information. I agree to hold harmless and for myself and my heirs or assignees and not to sue "Therapist Name", and any associates, including but not limited to, assistants, landlords or hosts for any reason as a result of my participation in this program/session(s). Any medical problems have been disclosed above. This includes, but is not limited to Heart Disease, H.I.V./AIDS, Hepatitis B, Tuberculosis etc.

I have read, understand, and agree to the above:

____
Date

____
Signature

____
Parent/Guardian Signature (for minors)

Treatment Plan

Business Name

Attending Therapist: ______________________

Name ______________________________ Date Init. Visit __________

Initial and Subsequent Treatment Plan(s)

Business Name
Client or Patient History

Client/Patient Name (Print) : ______________________________ Date: __________

Please supply the following:

1. Any medications that you are currently taking.

____
____
____

2. List any other prescription medications that you have taken within the last year.

____
____
____

3. List any physical problems that you have been treated for within the last 12 months.

____
____
____

4. Are you now seeing a physician for any health problems? __________ (Yes/No)

5. If yes, why (Re: #4): ______________________________
____
____
____

6. List any psychological or psychiatric issues or problems that you have been treated for.

____
____
____
____

7. Are you currently under the care of a psychologist, psychiatrist, counselor, social worker, or any other mental health professional? __________ (Yes/No)

8. If yes, why (Re: #7): ______________________________
____
____
____

9. Explain any other situations that you think could have a relationship on your visits here.

____
____
____

Client/Patient Signature: X______________________________

Please use the back of this form if you need additional space.

Business Name – Appointment Record Chart

Name: ______________________________ Date Init. Visit: __________

Date of Service	Visit #	Total # of Prepaid	Remaining Pre-paid	Notes

Client Sign

Date: ___________

Last Name: __________________ First Name: __________________ MI: __________

Address **(if changed)**____________________________________Apt./Suite__________________

City: ____________________________ State: ______________ Zip: ______________________

Day Phone: (____)____________ Eve. Phone: (____)____________ Fax: (___)__________

Email: ________________________

Signature: ____

Client Sign

Date: ___________

Last Name: __________________ First Name: __________________ MI: __________

Address **(if changed)**____________________________________Apt./Suite__________________

City: ____________________________ State: ______________ Zip: ______________________

Day Phone: (____)____________ Eve. Phone: (____)____________ Fax: (___)__________

Email: ________________________

Signature: ____

Client Sign

Date: ___________

Last Name: __________________ First Name: __________________ MI: __________

Address **(if changed)**____________________________________Apt./Suite__________________

City: ____________________________ State: ______________ Zip: ______________________

Day Phone: (____)____________ Eve. Phone: (____)____________ Fax: (___)__________

Email: ________________________

Signature: ____

The Importance of Follow-Up

Always be certain to follow up with clients/patients or prospective clients. Studies show that on average it takes seven contacts to make a sale. Also, keeping in touch with existing or past clients/patients reminds them of your service and shows them that you value their patronage. For prospective clients/patients a week after initial contact with them is fine. For existing or past clients/patients once a month is fine. You may also choose to contact them by postcard.

Call Back List

Cross Out Name When Call Back is Completed

Name	Last Appt Date	Call Back Date	Phone-Day	Phone: Night

Gift Certificate Sample

Gift certificates are a great way to encourage current clients/patients to pass the word to others. One way to encourage people to purchase gift certificates is by offering the gift certificates at a slightly reduced price. In that way the purchaser can give a gift that represents a greater value than is the actual cost to them. A ten percent discount is usually sufficient. It is important that you note the terms and conditions of the certificate. Stating that the certificate is not redeemable for cash, is not transferable, and stating an expiration date are all things you might consider including.

GIFT CERTIFICATE

Is a Gift to: *Mary Smith* ____________________

From: *John Smith* ____________________

It entitles the recipient named above to one session of the service named below, at

"NAME OF YOUR OFFICE"

Service: ____________________

This certificate must be used within 90 days of the date appearing hereon and is not redeemable or refundable for cash or other services. Any alteration will void this certificate. Certificate is non-transferable, and must bare an authorized signature from "YOUR OFFICE NAME" to be valid. Recipient will be required to fill our standard "YOUR OFFICE NAME" registration & release forms before this certificate can be used.

Authorized Signature: ____________________ *Date:* __________

I don't remember where I heard or read the statement below but I thought it was a great statement to have hanging on my wall.

Far to often people attempt to change their surroundings, circumstances, or the minds of others, when what they really need to start with is self-understanding. People will spend years in college or professional school to learn a profession or a trade. Few people spend even one week doing nothing but getting to know themselves. Only through self-knowledge can we make the valid decisions that will direct our lives in a positive way. Each of us must live our own lives. We have the responsibility; therefore we must take power in our lives. When we allow others to dictate our life's path or to control what is right or wrong for us, we invite sorrow.

You can't run away from your problems because everywhere you go you take yourself !

Author Unknown

Chapter 17

Sample Multi-purpose Induction

"Give the person a path, an image that he or she can identify with that represents his or her perception of a pleasant hypnotic state, and virtually any induction method will work."

Philip Holder, PhD.

PREPARATION

1. The Pre-talk

- Educate:
- What is hypnosis?
- Can I move?
- Myths
- Will I hear you?
- Enhance and give permission to use the imagination (Like a kid with a cardboard box)
- Let them know they have been in hypnosis
- Physical Manifestations many times
- Create Expectation
- Establish Rapport
- Alleviate any apprehension (fear)
- Gain Compliance
- Motivate

- Entertain
- Explain the importance of using their imagination
- Common Fears:
    - Can I get stuck in hypnosis?
    - Will I be able to do it right?
    - Can I be made to do or say something that I would otherwise not do?
    - Will I be able to drive home

2. Give them permission not to "Listen" to you. You will become background sound (As if listening to Dan Quail discuss potatoes or Nixon Checkers).

3. Give clients/patients the brush but don't paint the picture for them.

4. With groups keep the induction short: Often your group will be in less than perfect seats. Many may have back or neck problems or other reasons that will make it uncomfortable for them to remain in a seated position for extended periods of time.

5. Let them participate in the group intake / They must be invested in the process

Note: In a first group meeting the pre-talk and intake will be the body of the session. On the last meeting the later part of that session should be entertaining.

Multi-purpose Group Induction
(Can also be modified for individual sessions)
Sample From Group Session

INTRO:

It's important that you agree to follow what I ask you to do. It's in your best interest to follow my instructions. In hypnosis you cannot be made to do anything that you do not want to do. In fact, you could choose to refuse any suggestion or idea that I give you. You have the power to do that if you choose. If you do, I'll still get paid and you won't accomplish your goal. If you want to benefit and accomplish your goal I ask you to simply follow my suggestions and let it happen. From this moment forward I'd like you to imagine my words to be as real as they can be for you. Let my words become your reality. If you do that, you can accomplish your goal quickly and easily and I promise you'll have a wonderful experience.

Now make yourself comfortable. I want you to place your hands on your thighs. Place your feet on the floor and look up here. [If you have people lying down, have them pick a focal point on the ceiling]. Focus on me. Nothing else matters right now. In a few moments you're going to experience something wonderful… like a massage for the mind. So I want you to do absolutely nothing. More of nothing than ever before and leave everything to me. You have only one job… to enjoy. Take a mini-mental vacation and leave everything to me. Like when you're lying on the beach deeply relaxed. Even if there are hundreds of people talking and playing nearby it doesn't disturb you. You hear them but they are unimportant. They become nothing more than background noise. So look at me. Stare at me as if I were your favorite late night TV program. Imagine if you will, that it is late at night and as you watch me I want you to imagine your eyes growing a bit sleepy.

As you focus on me, I want you to drift back in time and imagine when you were a child and your wonderful imagination allowed you to easily transform that cardboard box into your special playhouse, fort, train, or car. When a simple toy would become so very real to you. Recapture that feeling you had as a small child and open up to that wonderful imagination that you have within. Let your imagination be your guide. Let my words become your reality. Watch how easy this is.

INDUCTION:

- I want you to take a deep breath in and fill up your lungs and hold it for a moment. Now look up at the ceiling. [PAUSE] Now exhale and close your eyes way down. Let go of every muscle joint, and fiber, as you let your body relax much more with each gentle breath you exhale. Just let every muscle go limp. Imagine that moment between awake and asleep when you drift gently away at night. Let your mind float, and drift, and dream. Now, I'd like you to imagine yourself in a safe and comfortable place of, peace, happiness, and pleasure. We'll call this place your Paradise of Perfect Relaxation. Go ahead now, create in your mind that special place that you can enjoy… a special place that's yours and yours alone. A place that no one else can go, not even in their dreams, unless you allow. A place of peace and comfort… and when you have that in idea or image in your mind, just nod your head so that I know you've got it. [Pause for a moment and look for responses]. Now hold that image in your mind for a while and enjoy. Any time that I ask you to return to "Your Special Place" I'd like you to bring back this image or feeling.

- In a moment I'm going to ask you to do something for me. In a moment I'm going to count from 1 to 3. When I reach the number 3, I'm going to say "open". When I say "open", I'd like you to open your eyes. When your eyes begin to gently open, allow your body to become even more relaxed and notice how good that feels. Quickly you'll notice your eyes becoming heavier, and when I say the word "sleep", I want you to close your eyes and relax even more deeply. Just let it happen and it will happen quickly and easily. When you close them feel a wave of relaxation as it drifts from the top of your head to the tips of your toes and just relax much more. Notice how easy this is.

- Here we go: 1,2,3, open. / Now sleep… Close your eyes down and just relax much more. Like that moment between awake and asleep as you return to your special place. Just let yourself go.

- In a moment I'm going to count from 1 to 3 again. When I reach the number 3, I'm going to ask you to open your eyes again. When I say "open", I want you to open your eyes and as you do… double your physical relaxation. Then when I say "sleep", close them down and relax even more.

- Here we go: 1,2,3, open. / Now sleep… Close them down and relax much more.

- In a moment I'm going to count from 1 to 3 one last time. When I reach the number 3, I'll say "open." When I do I want you to open your eyes and double your relaxation again. When I say "sleep," close them and you can relax even more deeply as a wonderful wave of relaxation drifts through your body.

- Here we go: 1,2,3, open. / Now sleep… Close them down and go even deeper into this wonderful quality of relaxation.

- And because it's normal and natural to relax when taking gentle breaths, from this moment forward, allow each and every gentle breath you exhale to carry you deeper into relaxation. Right now you have no place to go, nothing to do, and no problem to solve. This is your special time, so enjoy. Nothing else matters right now.

- Now you may or may not hear other sounds. It doesn't matter. In fact from this moment forward, any sounds, regardless of their source, will actually help to carry you deeper into this wonderful quality of relaxation, and you allow this to happen. It feels wonderful. And it keeps getting better.

- In a few moments I'm going to begin counting backwards from 5 to 1 and by the time I reach the number 1 (or sooner if you choose), you'll be in a deep and wonderful state of peace and tranquility… like a peaceful daydream. No matter how deeply you go into relaxation your subconscious mind will always hear the sound of my voice, and I can easily bring you out of hypnosis by counting from 1-3 and asking you to emerge. This is your special time. Nothing else matters right now. You will feel great. This is a special time to tap into that place of wisdom deep within you. It's easy if you simply do more of nothing than you've ever done before and allow it to happen. With each number simply imagine yourself drifting deeper into relaxation and it will happen easily. Just allow it to happen.

- On the count of 5, feel your body relaxing just like a rag doll. It's as if you were relaxing on the beach. White billowy clouds float above across a pale blue sky and as the waves roll in, by the time they reach the shoreline, they're just tiny little waves. And they drift back out so peacefully. Feel the warmth of the sun on your body, it feels so good, and as that warm wonderful feeling soaks in, every muscle, joint and fiber relaxes much more… it feels wonderful. A gentle refreshing breeze blows over any unclothed portions of your body. You feel wonderful, peaceful and calm, nothing can disturb you now. Each and every breath continues to carry you even deeper.

- And on the count of 4 notice how pleasantly heavy your body feels. Your head is so heavy now, the muscles of you neck so loose, limp, and relaxed, that even though you know you could move your head if you really wanted to it simply isn't worth the effort, and your head hangs loose and limp. Feels so good. Perfectly comfortable, peaceful, calm and relaxed. Each gentle breath you exhale carries you even deeper, and you simply allow that to happen. This is your special time, nothing else matters.

Now as each gentle breath carries you deeper into relaxation, let your body gently melt into relaxation. You may even begin to rest gently against the person next to you. It doesn't matter. You are in the company of good friends. You'll remain seated at all times and if you touch someone near you, you'll discover that it will actually help to carry you even deeper into relaxation. Each and every breath continues to carry you even deeper as you drift and float and dream.

- And on the count of 3 drifting even deeper… it's easy. Simply want it to happen and it will happen easily. It feels wonderful and curiously interesting to be so loose and limp, and relaxed. Within this quality of relaxation your arms may fall by your side, it doesn't matter. If that happens you'll discover that that will actually take you even deeper, and that's great.

- Drifting even deeper on the count of 2. Nothing else matters... This is your special time. The deeper you go the better you feel and the better you feel the deeper you go. Each and every breath continues to carry you even deeper.

- And on the next count it feels so good that you allow yourself to drift even deeper, drift to the deepest level available to you today... To that special place that's yours and yours alone. That special place where anything that you can imagine you can accomplish easily and effortlessly. Where anything you ever dreamed of is available to you. Where anything that you can imagine or visualize you can actualize. So drift very deeply now into this wonderful deep and beautiful sleep, very deeply on the count of 1.

- It feels wonderful. Each gentle breath continues to carry you deeper. You feel wonderful, refreshed, peaceful and calm. Floating, drifting, like in a beautiful dream only better, as a universe of happy thoughts drifts through your mind. You are in that place where anything you ever wanted or dreamed of is available to you. So stay and enjoy your special place. Stay and enjoy as my words go deep within empowering you to accomplish any goal easily.

Plain Language

GLOSSARY OF KEY TERMS

Aversion Therapy: An association, through hypnotic suggestion, of a negative stimuli, sensation, feeling, or image to the habit or behavior that the client or patient is attempting to change.

Client: A person who engages the services of a non-licensed and/or non-medical professional for the purpose of using hypnosis or hypnotherapy to accomplish his or her goal. (Laws vary from state to state. Check with the authorities in your jurisdiction.)

Direct Suggestion: A specific statement used to solicit a specific change in behavior or perception.

Emerge: To come out of the hypnotic state.

Indirect Suggestion: Suggestion structured in the form of metaphor.

Induction: A tool or mechanism used to induce a state of hypnosis

Intake: An information gathering interview where data is gathered from the client or patient for the purpose of helping the therapist or hypnotist understand the client or patient's goals, motivators, and any fears or obstructions that the person may have, and to solicit any information that will better enable the therapist or hypnotist to structure meaningful suggestion specific to that client or patients needs.

Maternal Inductions: Inductions that are nurturing, gentle, and passive.

Paternal Inductions (Authoritarian Inductions): Inductions where the hypnotist or therapist takes a more assertive position within the induction process.

Patient: Someone who is either seen by a licensed and/or medical professional or who is referred to the therapist by a licensed and/or medical professional (the patient of the medical professional).
(Laws vary from state to state. Check with the authorities in your jurisdiction.)

Pre-Talk: A part of the interview process where the therapist or hypnotist prepares the client, patient, or subject for the hypnotic process. The key elements of the pre-talk are to educate the client, patient, or subject, to create rapport, to create compliance, to alleviate fears, and to enhance the imagination.

Regression: A process whereby the client, patient, or subject is able to relive (in their mind) past events.

Subject: A person who is hypnotized for demonstration, research, or entertainment purposes.

Somnambulism: The depth of hypnosis needed for "durable suggestion" in a therapeutic session.

Waking Hypnotic Suggestion: Suggestion made to a client, patient, or subject when that person is still in a conscious waking state.

Triggers: Devices given to a client, patient, or subject that enable them to more powerfully bring back suggestions made in therapeutic session.

ORDER THESE GREAT COURSES TODAY INCREASE YOUR BASE OF KNOWLEDGE, DEVELOP YOUR SKILLS, IMPROVE YOUR SUCCESS RATE, INCREASE YOUR INCOME

CE1: Hypnosis and Hypnotherapy (Video Course)

Course Objectives: Understanding the concepts involved in hypnosis, is only the beginning. It is essential that the student be able to take these concepts and translate them into practical application. This course is intended to provide students with a format for practical application of the theories and concepts taught in our Hypnotherapy text course.

Soundtrack for your audio cassette player is available.

CE2: Practice Management I (Video Course)

Course Objectives: Having hypnosis/hypnotherapy skills is only one side of the equation. It is also important to have a working knowledge of practice management. This course is designed to help the student understand basic principles of practice management, advertising, etc. so as to provide a higher chance of success in professional practice.

CE3: Conduct an Effective Stop Smoking Session (Video Course)

Course Objectives: Smoke cessation is one of the main staples of a hypnotherapy practice. Successful smoke cessation sessions provide both income and referrals for other therapies. This video will provide insight into effective techniques that are conducive to an effective smoke cessation session.

CE4: Conduct an Effective Stress Management Session (Video Course)

Course Objectives: In recent years stress management has been an ever-growing part of most hypnotherapy practices. This course will help you to successfully provide clients with tools to manage stress and take back control of their lives.

CE5: How to Conduct an Effective Weight Loss Session (Video Course)

Course Objectives: Like smoke cessation, weight loss is one of the main staples of a hypnotherapy practice. Successful weight loss sessions provide both income and referrals for other therapies. This video will provide insight into effective techniques that will help you conduct more successful weight loss sessions.

CE6: Conducting An Effective Performance Enhancement Session (Video Course)

Course Objectives: Performance enhancement is a growing area of hypnotherapy. This course will help you to help your clients or patients overcome self-imposed barriers to success and to maximize their potential. Business, sports, and other personal goals are areas covered in this course.

CE7: How to Conduct an Effective Regression Session (Video Course)

Course Objectives: Most of the time direct and/or indirect suggestion, work effectively for positive change. There are many cases, however, where finding the root of the problem through regression is necessary. This course teaches both effective regression techniques, and to conduct a session without creating false memories.

CE8: Past Life Regression (Video Course)

Course Objectives: The theory of past lives is intriguing. Whether you are a believer or not, this course will provide you with insight into both the concept and the therapeutic value of past life experience.

CE9: Rapid Inductions (Video Course)

Course Objectives: In a clinical practice it is important to be able to achieve somnambulism in the shortest possible time. Speedy inductions with great depth are a great plus in your practice.

CE10: Meditation and Hypnosis (Video Course)

Course Objectives: What is trance? What similarities do they have? What differences do they have? What about "Self Hypnosis?" The answers to this and more are contained in this course.

CE11: Hypnotherapy (Text Course)

Course Objectives: This course provides an understanding of the theories and concepts in effect when using hypnosis. As well, case studies and examples are explored to provide students with insights into the actual response of clients/patients to hypnosis and hypnotherapy.

Pre-Talk – 2 Part Series

CE12 A: Conducting an effective Pre-Talk Part/Vol 1

Course Objectives: Perhaps the most important part of any hypnotherapy session is the pre-talk. This is where the hypnotherapist educates the client or patient, creates and/or strengthens rapport, and alleviates any client/patient fears. A great pre-talk can make the difference between success and failure in session. This videotape provides practical information and explains the components that should be part of a successful pre-talk thereby leading to greater success in session.

CE12B: Conducting an effective Pre-Talk, Part/Vol 2

Course Objectives: This course continues from Pre-Talk Vol.1, adding additional information, depth, and detail to the materials contained in the first section of the Pre-Talk training. These two tapes are a must for those practicing hypnosis or hypnotherapy.

Intake – 3 Part Series

CE13A: Conducting an Intake Video Course Vol./Part 1

Course Objectives: The intake, like the pre-talk is an essential component of successful session work. In the pre-talk, information flows from the therapist to the client or patient. In the intake, the information flows from the client or patient to the therapist. This is where the therapist gathers the information necessary for formulation of meaningful suggestions specifically tailored to the client or patient's needs. This tape will help you to conduct an effective intake.

CE13B: Conducting an Intake Video Course Vol./Part 2

Course Objectives: Continuing from Vol. 1 this course/tape goes into more detail and explanation regarding the intake process.

CE13C: Conducting an Intake Video Course Vol./Part 3

Course Objectives: Continuing from Vol. 2 this course/tape goes into more detail and explanation regarding the intake process. This 3-tape series is a must for the serious hypnotist or hypnotherapist.

CE14A: Conducting a Group Hypnosis/Hypnotherapy Session Vol 1

Course Objectives: Groups are a great way to increase your income, get referrals, and gain exposure in your market place. This videotape explains the way that groups can help your practice and will show you proven strategies and techniques for conducting group sessions. Dr. Holder demonstrates for you a group induction that is both quick and effective.

CE14B: Conducting a Group Hypnosis/Hypnotherapy Session Vol 2

Course Objectives: This course/tape provides continuing detail regarding the information contained in Vol.1. This set is a must for the serious hypnotist or hypnotherapist

CE14C: Conducting a Group Hypnosis/Hypnotherapy Session Vol 3

Course Objectives: Students ask Dr. Holder questions about group hypnosis and other material.

Elman Induction – 2 Volume Set

CE15A: The Elman Induction

Course Objectives: Want to induce hypnosis and achieve somnambulism in only 4 to 5 minutes? The Elman induction is a rapid induction that when properly executed enables the therapist to achieve somnambulism with the vast majority of clients/patients on virtually each session… even on the first session. Dr. Holder will take you through each step of this exciting induction. He will explain how and why it is such a great induction. If you have never used the Elman induction this tape will show you how. If you already use this induction this video may very well give you greater insight into ways to make your induction even better.

CE15B: The Elman Induction

Course Objectives: This tape explains in greater detail the information covered in Vol./Tape 1. This tape is invaluable in gaining a complete understanding of Elman Vol. 1.

CE16A: Fundamentals of Hypnosis and Hypnotherapy Vol. 1

The Fundamentals of hypnosis are covered in this series. This 2 tape series covers all of the essential information that students new or old need to know about hypnosis. It is a great place to start for the beginner, and a great place for those with experience to firm up their knowledge of core information.

CE16B: Fundamentals of Hypnosis and Hypnotherapy Vol. 2

This course/tape continues where Vol./Part 1 leaves off. It is a great place to start for the beginner, and a great place for those with experience to firm up their knowledge of core information.

CE17A: Questions and Answers Vol. 1

Students ask assorted questions about hypnosis. Dr. Holder answers the group's questions. This tape contains many of the common questions and answers that both students and practicing hypnotists and hypnotherapists often have.

CE17B: Questions and Answers Vol. 2

Students ask assorted questions about hypnosis. Dr. Holder answers the group's questions. This tape contains many of the common questions and answers that both students and practicing hypnotists and hypnotherapists often have.

INTRODUCTION TO HYPNOSIS AND HYPNOTHERAPY

If you want to increase your client or patient's level of comfort with hypnosis and make your pre-talk more effective, play this videotape for your client or patient prior to bringing them into your therapy room for their formal pre-talk and intake. By having the client or patient watch this videotape in advance, many of their questions are already answered by the time they sit down with you. This tape is designed to save the therapist time and to make the pre-talk go more smoothly and more quickly. You can even have your receptionist play this tape for your next client or patient while you are in session with another person. This tape is a time-saver and does wonders to make your client or patient feel more secure with the process of hypnotherapy by answering many common questions in advance.

SEVEN DAYS TO GREAT MEDITATION

This is a great tape for anyone who would like to get the most out of meditation. Gaining the ability to achieve meditative trance state can take months or even years of practice the conventional way. With this tape the ability to achieve a meditative state can take as little as seven days. Dr. Holder has been teaching meditation for decades. Combined with his extensive knowledge of hypnosis and hypnotherapy he has designed this tape to help others more easily experience the wonderful benefits of meditation. This tape can provide a way to get rid of stress and to open up to your creative abilities, your intuitive abilities, and to your untapped talents.

Ask About Our
Distance Learning Home Study
Hypnotherapy Certification Course
Earn your Hypnotherapy Certification at Home

Contact Master's Center for a Current Catalogue

Master's Center also has great Kung-Fu tapes. We would be happy to send you our Kung Fu tape catalogue